CW00672675

Dominatrix

Dominatrix

A MEMOIR

THE MAKING OF
MISTRESS CHLOE

headline

First published in 2002
by HEADLINE BOOK PUBLISHING

10 9 8 7 6 5 4 3 2 1

Cataloguing in Publication Data
is available from the British Library

ISBN 0 7553 1013 6

Text design by Jane Coney
Typeset by Palimpsest Book Production Limited,
Polmont, Stirlingshire
Printed and bound in Great Britain by
Mackays of Chatham, PLC

HEADLINE BOOK PUBLISHING
A division of Hodder Headline
338 Euston Road
London NW1 3BH

www.headline.co.uk
www.hodderheadline.com

Contents

CHAPTER ONE

A Lesson in Grammar

The Human Washing Machine confounded My expectations. From his scouse fishmonger's accent, I'd expected off-the-rack Marks and Sparks, rumpled, forty-five, bleary-eyed, balding, and boozy. What presented itself at My dungeon not only on time, but in fact two minutes early, was Emporio Armani, maybe twenty-eight, tall and fit-looking, with the self-delighted air of one who'd never been picked anything other than first for any team at school. I knew I'd seen him somewhere.

He displayed a great many very white teeth and said, 'I'm Chris.' His breath suggested that he'd fortified himself with a couple of pints before coming over. He was apparently accustomed to turning people to putty with his smile, which I was pretty sure I recognised from a mobile telephone advert. I was going to enjoy wiping every last vestige of it off his face.

I left him standing in the door and returned to My throne. 'Well, would it be all right if I came in then?' he chuckled, insufficiently bright to be discomfited. I just glared at him. The better part of a minute went by, neither of us budging. At last he deferred, looking down, exhaling, sawing the bottom of his nose with his forefinger. 'Well,' he said.

Still I glared. He glanced up at Me, and then away again. I was pretty certain by now that he was quite a well known footballer, a celebrated Premiership striker, and that I'd seen him on telly, mumbling macho banalities down an interviewer's microphone as I channel-surfed. For a fraction of a moment, or maybe it wasn't that long, I wished that I were sufficiently interested in sport to be able to identify him. He cleared his throat. He seemed an inch shorter than a moment before.

'You were told, boy,' I finally said, taking a very long time on 'boy', cramming it with disdain, 'to be here at three.'

He looked at his wristwatch, which had probably cost him more than My dad used to make, before he got his greengrocery, in six months of selling Hoovers. 'But it's only just three now,' he protested.

'Which means,' I purred, 'that you must have arrived at around 2:58, does it not, boy?'

He gulped. Blood rushed to his face. He had one of those complexions that keeps no secrets.

'I thought,' he said, 'that you'd prefer that I err on the side of . . .'

'Silence!' I hissed, hurtling so suddenly off my throne at him that his eyes widened. 'On your knees!' He dropped as though the invisible string that had been holding him aloft had just been snipped. I love when they do that. I stood four inches from him, letting his nostrils fill with My perfume, giving him a lovely long look at My waist. 'Clasp your hands behind your back, maggot,' I commanded, 'and touch your forehead to the floor.' He whimpered and complied. I love when they whimper. He was exuding less self-assurance by the second.

'My feet, boy,' I purred. 'They need kissing.' I'd have liked to have stepped on the back of his head, but had nothing to hold on to; My abilities haven't yet come to include balancing on one foot in a platform shoe with a nine-inch (and no, I'm not exaggerating) stiletto heel. They may never do. He kissed.

I stepped backwards, out of his reach. 'I thought I told you to kiss My feet, boy,' I said. You should have seen his expression. There was no mistaking that the prospect of having to slide forward on his knees was just horrendous for him, as it was likely to scuff the knees of his Armani trousers irreversibly. I slapped him across the face. Such was his fairness that My handprint remained on his cheek, as though in a cartoon. I kept myself from giggling and grabbed a handful of his wonderful thick hair, pulling his head back. 'And you will not under any circumstances presume to address Mistress in the second person. Is that quite clear, boy?'

He gulped again. English presumably hadn't been his long suit at school. 'Sorry, madam?'

That got him slapped again, harder. 'First person is *I*,'

I reminded him, tightening My grip on his hair, eliciting a wonderful small gasp, 'or, in the plural . . .'

'*We*?' he ventured in a very small voice.

'What a clever boy!' I marvelled. 'Third person is *he*, *she*, *it*, and, in the plural form, *they*. So what do you suppose is the second?'

There was sweat on his smooth pink brow. I love to make sweat appear. I pulled even harder on his hair, and he gasped louder than the first time. 'I don't know,' he blurted.

I slapped him on behalf of all the underpaid English teachers to whom he'd paid insufficient attention over the years. '*You*,' I said, 'you extremely naughty, inattentive boy. *You* is the second person. Now you – and in what person am I speaking, boy?'

'Second,' he gasped as I pulled even harder on his hair.

'Wonderful! Yes, exactly. You will take great care never again to address Mistress in the second person, any more than you would address Her Majesty the Queen in so familiar a way. Is that quite clear, boy? You will refer to Me in the third person, as Mistress, you see. And you will never use any form of the first person – not I, not me, not my or mine – in relation to your utterly pathetic self. Is that too quite clear?'

I'd have bet you a bundle that he hadn't any idea what I was on about, but he nonetheless agreed eagerly. 'Thus,' I said, 'rather than "I hope Mistress will deign to wash her underwear in My mouth," you – and note once again the second person – would instead say . . .'

He winced, expecting another slap. I love when they wince – but not as much as I love confounding their expectations; I let go of his hair and didn't lay another finger on him. '"Mistress's obedient boy hopes Mistress will deign to wash her underwear in its mouth." Do you see how easy it is, boy?'

'Yes, Mistress. I do see.'

This slap hurt him more for his not having braced for it. 'Who sees?' I demanded.

He was back to blurting. 'Mistress's obedient boy! Mistress's obedient boy sees!'

I left him kneeling and returned to My throne. There was an unmistakable bulge in his trousers. My pointing it out to him made the handprint disappear from his cheek, all of which now turned the colour the handprint had been. I reckoned that what had excited him most was My reference to having My underwear in his mouth. 'My fantasy,' he'd revealed in his first email to Me, 'is being restrained and forcefed one at a time Your weekly load of underware to wash in my mouth to remove any stubborn staines.' Spelling hadn't been his strong suit at school, but he'd got points for capitalizing Your.

I told him to remove his clothing. He stripped down to his briefs, folding his trousers, jacket, and shirt with more care than most new mothers expend putting nappies on their infants. He was quite gorgeously muscular from top to bottom. You could tell that he was trying to figure out a way to turn to minimise the embarrassment of his tumescence. Mistress was having none of it. I told him to bring Me his clothing. On his knees. My doing so didn't help with the embarrassment in his briefs, not even a bit.

'You've done such a lovely job folding everything,' I said. 'I can imagine that you're quite the boy to have round before a dinner party to make sure everyone's serviette is just so.' He was breathing audibly by now. I stood up and tossed his clothing back over My shoulder. He inhaled sharply. His whole world was being pulled apart, what with his suit no longer being tidily folded. And it was obviously exciting him a treat.

I handcuffed his wrists and ankles to the St Andrew's cross, pausing a couple of times to swat with annoyance at his willie, snarling, 'You will keep that horrid little thing out of Mistress's way, boy, or I'll have it off.' Which had the effect of putting it even more in the way, of course.

I produced a bag of clothes pegs. My sense was that he wasn't a full-out pain slut, but often even those who don't fancy actual suffering are transported by the threat of it. I was wrong about this one. 'After you've cleaned My panties, I of course will want to hang them out to dry,' I told him, 'so I'd better have a few of these handy. Any ideas where I might keep them in view, boy?'

He nearly swooned with excitement. I stuck a thick black rubber dildo in his mouth to keep him quiet and attached a pair to his nipples. He writhed in agontasy, that remarkable hybrid that women of my calling observe so regularly. But for the dildo, you might have heard him back on the pitch.

'That penalty kick you missed last season against Wigan,' I said, bluffing wildly, not entirely sure that Wigan even had a Premiership team, or that he wasn't in it. 'That broke My brothers' hearts, you know. They were inconsolable for days.'

He looked up at me perplexedly. I backhanded him across the face. I won't have a submissive making eye contact with Me. 'I don't know what Mistress means,' he said. 'We didn't even play the Latics. They're not even in the Premiership.'

I twisted his nipples. He howled. 'If Mistress says it was Wigan you missed the kick against, worm, who was it you missed the kick against?'

'Wigan!' he blurted. 'I remember now! It was definitely the Latics!' I yanked his briefs down to his knees and attached half a dozen clothes pegs to his balls. The sweat was coming off him in sheets now, and you could have driven nails with his erection.

His moaning stabilised. I removed the dildo from his mouth. 'On second thought, no,' I said, and jammed it back in before flicking at the clothes peg on his right nipple. God, was he enjoying himself! I went to the closet and got the three pairs of panties I'd culled from my laundry basket that morning. I returned to him and made as though about to flick one of the clothes pegs on his scrotum. He squirmed in panic. I laughed My cruellest laugh and flicked one on a nipple instead.

You're wondering if inflicting pain excites Me. It doesn't. If I had My way, I'd restrict my practice to crossdressers, fetishists, and others who would be content to admire a particular part of My costume while I ridiculed them for it. Taxi drivers don't enjoy transporting passengers with severe body odour. Stockbrokers are unhappy when stocks they've recommended highly perform poorly. Major international film stars are substantially displeased when autograph-seekers besiege them in restaurants. No one enjoys 100 per cent of his working day.

I don't enjoy inflicting pain, but I do quite fancy conferring pleasure, and that's exactly what I was doing with this guy. It's no more My place – or yours! – to tell him that he mustn't derive pleasure from having clothes pegs attached to his nipples than it is to tell the labourer across the road that he mustn't revel in the protuberances of the girl on Page 3 of his tabloid, or your mate Angela that she absolutely mustn't picture Pierce Brosnan when she masturbates. To each his own, innit?

In any event, I reminded him that the previous week had been unseasonably warm and very humid, and asked if he'd found himself sweating a lot. He couldn't answer for the dildo halfway down his throat, but that didn't keep Me from flicking one of the lower clothes pegs to punish him for failing to answer. I told him I'd felt quite clammy much of the week, and that My panties were thus in need of an especially thorough washing. The poor devil was absolutely beside himself with excitement. I yanked out the dildo and jammed a pair of panties where it had been. You'd never seen such ecstatic twitching. I wondered if he'd rip the handcuffs right out of the wall.

I flicked one of his nipple pegs and demanded that he spit out the first pair of panties, replacing it immediately with the next. As he worked on it, I gave him a lovely long look at the third, by far the laciest and tartiest of the three. In fact, when he'd confirmed his appointment the afternoon before, I'd dashed out and bought them, just to make them smell of Me in time for him. The guy was never going to get closer to Heaven than this. If I'd uncuffed one hand and asked him to sign his house and car over to Me at that moment, there's little question that he would have done so.

I did indeed free one hand so that he could play with himself. I returned to My throne and watched him. He took his time. I mentally compiled a list of things I needed from Tesco. I remembered yearning in vain at thirteen for a coat of the sort in which other little reggae enthusiasts my age looked so chic.

I wondered if Mum, who'd had a frightful cold, were feeling better yet.

He finally ejaculated rather more voluminously than I'm accustomed to – most of My punters are such implacable wankers that they never store up a great deal of semen – and sagged contentedly on his cross.

'Tell Me, boy,' I demanded, yawning contemptuously. 'Have you enjoyed your time with Mistress?'

'More than I – more than Mistress's obedient boy! – can begin to describe, Mistress.' He dared an adoring glance at Me, a glance for which he would receive his hardest slap across the face yet. I can't bear it when, because you've allowed them to ejaculate in your presence, they suddenly imagine themselves in love with you.

I flicked one of the clothes pegs below his waist. It got his attention, and brought out the true submissive. 'Thank you, Mistress,' he blurted reflexively.

I held My hands to either side of the pegs on his nipples, making him shiver with foreboding. 'Before you're dismissed, boy, a few questions. Whose exclusive property are you from this afternoon forward?'

His reflexes failed him. He said nothing. I swatted the clothes pegs. It seemed to accelerate the flow of blood to his brain. 'Mistress Chloe's,' he yelped. 'I'm Mistress's – no, Mistress's obedient boy is – Mistress Chloe's exclusive property.'

'What a remarkably clever little man,' I purred mockingly. 'And whose word is your law, boy?'

'Mistress Chloe's!' He was catching on with remarkable rapidity.

'Exactly right,' I pretended to marvel. 'And who is the supreme dominant goddess of all London?'

'Mistress Chloe is!' he fairly sang. 'Mistress Chloe is the supreme dominant goddess of all London!'

'And you won't miss any more penalty kicks when My brothers and their mates are emotionally invested in your scoring them?'

He thought we were finished. Grinning, he sneaked a peek at me. And got slapped very hard for it.

Heading home on the Metropolitan line, the supreme dominant goddess of all London had to stand between Baker Street and Preston Road in spite of the fact that her feet were absolutely killing her after a long afternoon in nine-inch stiletto heels, and was jostled twice and apologised to not even once by a malodorous large teen who bellowed into his mobile phone between Finchley Road and Wembley Park so that you might have heard him in Leicester Square.

CHAPTER TWO

A New Convert to Kink

I wasn't born a dominatrix. Indeed, if I hadn't attended that party in Hampstead in May 1986, I might never have realised that I might one day enjoy becoming one.

The house in which I first glimpsed the proverbial writing on the wall was just like any other in Hampstead – except with a driveway full of Ferraris, Lamborghinis, and Roller limousines, the latter disgorging an endless succession of glamourpusses in figure-hugging gleaming leather and latex and PVC. My boyfriend, who'd scored coke or something for the house's owner, fairly hurtled from the cab. There were likely, after all, to be sexual adventurers afoot he hadn't yet charmed, and not a minute to lose.

I paid the driver, whose eyes were halfway out of his head, let myself out of his cab, and made my way gingerly up to the front door in my extremely not-designed-for-walking-in red pumps. A square-jawed man approximately the size of the house I'd grown up in, pierced more prolifically than anyone I'd ever seen, smiled warmly, revealing glittery insets in his two front teeth. 'I am delighted to welcome you,' he said very earnestly, as though reciting a line it had taken him a good long while to commit to memory.

A timid little voice inside me said, 'Are you quite mad? Do you honestly imagine you'll fit in with these people?' It was the voice of the Mouse, the hopelessly shy, dutiful little daughter of the suburbs I'd been in early adolescence. 'Sod off,' I growled at her under my breath, inadvertently alarming the big glittery smile man, and walked gingerly in.

Major sensory overload! A band that hoped to remind you of the Velvet Underground, complete with fingernails-across-blackboard electric viola, was screeching away in the cavernous living room. Either Wolverhampton Wanderers had shipped down the socks and jock straps they'd collected over the course of the season, or a great deal of amyl nitrate was being snorted; I recognised the smell from the days when I spent half my free hours at gay discos. When the band stopped for a moment, I thought I heard monks chanting. Monks! Every step of the enormous spiral staircase to my right was illuminated by tiny candles. I reeled. 'Very nice,' the Mouse sniffed. 'Well, time to go home. You haven't got a VCR yet and there's *Gardener's World* to watch.'

I ignored her and made myself check in my coat, without

which I felt pretty nearly naked in my shiny black PVC leotard, cut very high at the hips to expose as much of my not-yet-famous legs as possible. I took a deep breath, and another, and a third, and marched with heart pounding more loudly than the band's bass drum across the living room. I didn't go unnoticed by the leering glamourpusses watching from the balcony above. If I had, mind you, I might not have come out of my bedroom again for six or seven years, as I'd left no stone unturned in making myself as ravishing as possible.

I'd never owned a pair of shoes with higher heels. Indeed, there had been a time in my life when I'd have bet you that no one could walk five steps in such footwear without breaking her neck. My elegant shoulder-length black opera gloves complemented the narrow black studded collar around my neck. And I hadn't worked so hard on my makeup in years. My black eyeliner swept lavishly up and outwards. There were gold highlights on my brows, rose blusher on my cheeks. No harlot in King's Cross that night had redder lips. Superdrug didn't sell a paler ivory base. I'd gilded the lily and worn my waist-length blonde wig.

I felt a gratifying number of eyes on me as I made my way across the room and staked out an expanse of wall space from which to pretend to be very interested in the band until something better presented itself. I wondered if the house's owner had somehow managed to get hold of the SS's decorator. Ponderous red and velvet drapes covered every window, not to mention most of the walls, from which brass eagles glowered intimidatingly down. A bar ran the whole depth of the room on one side. It was lined by persons whose attire made mine seem in comparison like that of a substitute teacher at Pinner Grammar School. The floor was sunken in the middle, where more gleaming hedonists sprawled on black leather sofas.

I realised that someone was speaking to me, a man on the sofa I was standing behind. He was around forty-five, with a bald spot and a ponytail and a gap between his front teeth. He wore nothing but a pair of shiny black latex briefs and a studded dog collar, to which was attached a leash held by a rather equine lady companion.

I put my hand to my ear to indicate my inability to hear him over the fingernails on blackboard. He rose up a little from the sofa and spoke again. No improvement. I bent over and turned my ear towards him.

'You're wearing such wonderful shoes!' he said.

'And you, such wonderful briefs,' I replied, just as the violist decided that we were in insufficient discomfort and turned his amplifier up. Mr Latexbriefs grinned and shrugged apologetically. His date tugged at the leash. He shouted into her ear. She looked up at me and then down at my shoes. She shouted into his ear. They both laughed. I felt very much a gooseberry, and feared, as the violist was now playing a solo in a register forbidden by the Geneva Convention, that at any second I might start bleeding out of my ears all over my fellow revellers. I decided that the upper floors of the house needed looking at.

Immediately I rejoiced in my decision. Ascending the magnificent candlelit staircase, I was beamed at and greeted like a long-lost friend by most of the glamourpusses arrayed on it. Behold the power of PVC, extremely impractical footwear, and too much makeup, I thought.

Reaching the first landing, I peeked curiously into an eerily illuminated bedroom. On the four-poster bed in the centre of the room, an attractive couple cavorted, oblivious to the fact that fascinated onlookers surrounded them on all sides. The vaguely Italianate woman, handcuffed to the bed's four posts, wore a black PVC skirt that exposed all of her bottom save for those horizontal strips that narrow buckles traversed. Her arse was covered in bruises.

She squirmed with excitement as her partner, whose long-eyelashed prettiness was that of a seventies department store mannequin, ran his finger slowly between her cheeks. Then he whacked her with a paddle, causing her to cry out. He pulled her head back with a handful of her hair and held the paddle in front of her face for her to kiss dutifully. I noticed that at least one of the male onlookers was rigid with excitement.

'Absolutely appalling,' the Mouse sniffed. But there could be no mistaking the look on the face of the paddled woman as being that of anything other than rapture.

In the adjoining bedroom, a strobe light flashed. Three naked men were chained to the wall, backs outwards. I wanted to investigate. A slim woman with a becomingly spiky wig and features too fine and uniform not to have benefited from the help of a cosmetic surgeon stood in my way, brazenly eyeing me up and down. 'Nice,' she decided. 'Very nice.' She handed me a playing card, the four of clubs. 'For the raffle,' she explained, pointedly putting her hand on my shoulder as she leaned. Even on the second floor the band was making conversation difficult. I got the impression that I might have coaxed her into a dark corner without too much difficulty, but her plasticity put me off.

Once inside the room, I realised that the three chained men were the prisoners of a petite fiftyish woman in a red latex catsuit that she was too expansive in the arse to have worn. Smoking through a long, rhinestone-bedecked cigarette holder that she periodically entrusted to the collared man kneeling beside her, she brandished an implement that sparked when she touched it to her prisoners' bare backsides. 'Violet wand,' someone shouted helpfully into my ear. It was my boyfriend, apparently recharging for a moment between encounters. The three chained men writhed in dread, waiting for the catsuit lady to touch her apparatus to their arses. When she did, they shrieked and twitched like epileptics.

'Absolutely appalling,' the Mouse sniffed. 'Well,' I had to acknowledge, 'not my own cuppa.'

There was no sign of my boyfriend now. I needed a drink after the violet wand room, and went back downstairs to the bar. The Velvets wannabes stopped playing, and the bass player announced that they would be taking a fifteen-minute break. Waves of delight and relief broke across the room. I ordered a vodka and orange. A record nearly as annoying as the band in its relentless thuddiness had begun to play at an immoderate volume. A couple began to dance a little uncertainly and then, realising that no one was following suit, returned sheepishly to the bar.

A tall very toothy man with a prodigious mop of fading brown hair was standing beside me, grinning enormously. He'd had some sort of fibrous veg with his dinner; there was a strand of it between his teeth. I smiled at him nonetheless. This seemed to confuse him, and he looked quickly away. I sipped my drink and, as I often do in idle moments, set about determining which person in view I'd most enjoy being trapped with in a comfortably appointed lift for a couple of hours. I realised that Toothy was trying to get my attention.

'Please, Mistress? Permission to worship Mistress's beautiful feet?'

Hello? Worship my feet? As one in a place not yet redeemed by Christianity might worship a graven idol? What was he *on* about?

Often our mouths get busy well before our brains get wind of the project. Sometimes, though, we think too long before speaking. Mistaking my silence for affirmation, Toothy had collapsed to his knees, and now was covering the toe of my right shoe with little kisses. 'Run,' the Mouse thought aloud. 'Wait,' I implored her. 'I have to admit I quite fancy this.'

He continued along the sides of my foot, round the back, and then began licking the whole length of the six-inch heel. 'And now the other,' I heard someone snarl impatiently. I realised that someone was I. When he didn't hear me, I impulsively grabbed a handful of his wonderful thick hair and tilted his face towards my own, as I'd seen the guy in the first bedroom upstairs do. The poor sod was absolutely transported with joy. Why had no one told me it was so easy?

Glowering down at him, I pointed to my other foot. He had at it eagerly. A couple of my fellow revellers turned to watch, and then a couple more. I was in the spotlight, and how deeply pleasurable its glow!

How to get away, though? Would I now have to stand there

for the rest of the evening with Toothy slobbering on my pumps? Oh, for the applicable protocol!

It occurred to me that we were very much in Lewis Carroll territory, that many things were the exact opposite of what they appeared. Through cruelty, these people expressed great affection for one another. The more disdainfully the dominants addressed the submissives, the more the subs seemed to revel in it. I pulled Toothy up by his hair again and hissed, 'You are dismissed now, worm,' into his ear. And I'd thought he looked transported before! As he scurried dutifully away on all fours, how was I supposed not to chuckle aloud?

The woman in the backless PVC skirt I'd watched being paddled upstairs mounted the little bandstand and spoke into a microphone. 'Raffle time, everyone,' she announced. Her faint German accent quite suited her, I thought. She was joined by a pair of conspicuously gorgeous persons, one of each sex, in suspendered corsets, stockings, gloves, and high heels, both with a thick, studded collar. The guy who'd been doing the paddling unsealed a deck of playing cards and spilled it into a large glass bowl, which he held up to the paddle lady. She made a big display of holding one gloved hand over her eyes before reaching in. 'The seven of diamonds,' she announced, holding the card aloft.

Someone in the crowd whooped jubilantly, as though at a game-winning goal. A swarthy middle-aged guy with manicured facial hair and a great many earrings hurried forward, brandishing his seven of diamonds. The paddle lady embraced him in congratulation and offered him a gift-wrapped box. It turned out to contain a leash. He attached it to the collar of the beaming female raffle prize. Everyone laughed and applauded as he led her off.

The paddle lady reached once more into her bowl. 'The four of clubs,' she announced, and the room began to spin. 'That's you!' the woman beside me, seeing the card in my hand, exulted. I felt every drop of blood in my body rushing to my face; little wonder that I was so weak in the knees. Every eye in the place was on me.

'Well, go on then,' someone behind me said encouragingly, and the next thing I knew, I was being awarded a congratulatory embrace and gift-wrapped leash by the paddle lady, and bathing in the first applause I'd received in over a decade. My prize winked at me. If anything, I'd underestimated his gorgeousness before. The Mouse, doubtless pouting, stayed mum.

'But what am I to do with him?' I whispered in the paddle lady's ear.

She laughed. 'Whatever it amuses you to do with him. For as long as you remain at the party, he's your possession.'

I have to admit that I rather enjoyed the thought of that. And by the time I finally went home, not long before the sun was expected to peek over the horizon, I was the United Kingdom's most fervent new convert to kink.

CHAPTER THREE

Backwards Through a Hedge

Actually, there's much heated debate about whether It All Really Began at that party in Hampstead, or one evening in the late sixties when my parents drove, with me in the back seat, past The Roundhouse in Chalk Farm, in those days a notable rock venue. On the steps in front loitered a group of impossibly gorgeous young rebels oozing confidence in their tight leather, black lace, and red lipstick. They were simply the most beautiful sight I'd ever beheld, and I'd been to the local Odeon to see *The Sound of Music*. As I stared openmouthed at them, quite unable to look away, I resolved that one day I too would slouch defiantly outside a notable rock venue, inspiring awe in another daughter of the suburbs.

It turned out that there would be more than a few slips 'twixt cup and lip.

When I was around ten, my entrepreneurial spirit manifested itself after I saw an advert in the *Melody Maker* for the Temple discotheque in Wardour Street and decided on the spot to run my own weekly disco – in Theresa Basire's back garden, because my own parents took a dim view of children running amok on their carefully manicured lawn and flower beds. I reckoned it was high time the kids who met regularly to play in the alley that ran along the back of our house learned, to whatever extent we British are capable, to dance. Theresa's parents, good sorts whose own back garden resembled scrubland, watched warily from their kitchen window as I plugged my Dansette record player into the extension cable thoughtfully provided by Mr Basire, strung up some fairy lights, and waited for the board on which I'd painted an exact copy of the Temple logo to catch prospective punters' little eyes.

Instant success! There must have been at least nine there that first hot summer night, nibbling crisps and peanuts, sipping the orangeade jointly provided by several sets of parents, and dancing to Desmond Dekker, none more animatedly than I, in my two-tone burgundy flares and burnt orange tie-dye top.

Be still, my heart! Douglas Hughson, the best-looking boy in the alley gang, widely expected to go on to win Wimbledon, was approaching. And inviting me to come over the following weekend to meet some of his friends.

*   *   *

The big day arrived.

'Ever played strip poker?' Douglas asked. All his mates seemed to be male, and his parents seemed not to be at home. Desperate to appear neither stupid nor naive, I admitted I hadn't, but would give it a go, and of course almost immediately found myself down to my top and knickers. Naturally I lost the next hand too.

'Off!' they chanted eagerly. 'Off! Off! Off!'

Inexpressibly embarrassed, I retreated behind the sofa and, pleading with the boys to stay where they were, peeled off my panties. Whereupon Douglas and his friends leapt as one from their seats to glimpse the heretofore unglimpsable.

'I saw it!' one of them exulted. 'I *saw* it!' I hurriedly put my panties back on and said goodbye with as much dignity as I could muster. Walking home, my face burning with humiliation, I was sure that passing motorists and pedestrians could tell from looking at me that I'd been bad. The thought of how my parents would react if they found out made me cry so hard that I had to stop at the end of my road to compose myself.

After Roxeth Junior, Ealing Grammar School was a very different kettle of fish – one that made me squeamish. Indeed, as I stood in the Assembly Hall on my first morning, I was so sick with nerves I was sure I would vomit, which could only have improved the appearance of my revolting two-sizes-too-big yellow and brown school uniform. On a good day, a sociologist might have allowed my family on to the lowest rung of the middle-class ladder, and I was aware of how my parents had struggled to save the money to buy me everything the school had said I'd need. 'You'll grow into it,' my mother, sewing name labels into my navy-blue school knickers in our sunny back garden, tried to reassure me.

Not if the first girl with whom I interacted had anything to do with it. She was quite the fiercest-looking girl I'd ever seen, with the worst acne, and living proof both that the best things don't always come in the smallest packages, and that men aren't the only ones with Napoleonic complexes. She came up to the base of my throat, into which she seemed to want desperately to sink her incisors. I smiled weakly. She glowered more fiercely. 'I'm going to make you wish,' she predicted, 'that your mum and dad had never met,' and left me standing there feeling more alone, terrified, and miserable than I'd ever dreamed possible. Welcome to Ealing Grammar School!

It got worse. In the shower room, after PE, my new classmates proudly showed one another their first bras. Breasts to the left of me, breasts to the right, and I as curvaceous as the pavement in front of my parents' house.

As though, perhaps, to prime the proverbial pump, my mother bought me a tiny bra with blue and white flowers on it. It hung off me.

Given my innate high intelligence, I must have found some consolation in the classroom, though, right? Wrong. My maths teacher, perhaps the most implacable sadist I've ever met – and I've attended a great, great many BDSM parties and events over the years – delighted in singling me out to humiliate with the impossible equations he scrawled on the board. Halfway back in his classroom, I couldn't even read the bloody numbers. When I stammered, he bellowed. In a BDSM 'scene', the submissive is always given a special word with which to signal that he's had enough. In Mr Bunion's Ealing Grammar School maths class, there were no safe words. The only way I could stop the torture was to burst into tears. Doing so, of course, inspired wholesale admiration on the part of my classmates.

As I sat gloomily in his surgery, squinting hopelessly at the blurred eye chart on the wall, my optician decreed that I was shortsighted. The good news was that the condition was correctable with glasses. The bad news was that the condition was correctable with glasses. This couldn't be happening to me.

I comforted myself with the knowledge that things surely could get no worse, whereupon they almost immediately did. I could either wear a brace day and night for the next six months, my dentist informed my parents, or, as an adult, resemble Bugs Bunny. Wasn't a little embarrassment in the short term, my mum took me aside to suggest, preferable to a lifetime of ridicule? I could barely hear her over my own sobbing.

Almost overnight I lost every trace of the confidence I'd had in such abundance as the bossy little dickens who'd masterminded every prank and game in her pre-teen peer group and commandeered a neighbour's back garden for her discotheque. I shrank from contact with others. At break time I huddled alone in a corner, trying in vain to will myself to a wonderful land where mere mention of bras and glasses and teeth braces was punishable by death.

But I didn't want for social interaction. Every time she saw me in the playground, in fact, Rachel Talbot, the malevolent young Pygmy I'd encountered on my first morning, would dash over to throttle me, while her delightful henchwomen formed a jeering circle. Terrified and humiliated to the marrow, I'd pray to be struck by lightning. The sky never obliged.

Even those who loved me most betrayed me, if unwittingly. Such was the style in which my mother insisted I wear my hair that even my form teacher felt called upon to marvel at my seeming to have been dragged backwards through a hedge. And then the *coup de grâce*: the ever-more-popular Douglas Hughson, who seemed not to remember me, wittily, quite publicly, nicknamed me the Mouse.

If these were the happiest days of my life, I wished for a mercifully short one.

You ache for some biographical minutiae. I can't bear to see you in discomfort. I grew up in the safe, extremely boring Harrow suburb of Ruislip, near to where it merges, almost imperceptibly, with Ickenham. Modern nutritionists agree that one should eat five portions of fruit and vegetables per day. As a child, I probably ate ten, for the very good reason that my dad, a Yorkshireman who'd been an RAF pilot during the war, was a greengrocer, and not just any greengrocer, mind you, but the one to whom nearly all the best chefs in northwest Harrow (no sniggering!) came for their fruit and veg. I was eating kiwi fruit before most of my little classmates even knew what a peach was, guavas and mangoes years before the UK release of the first Bob Marley & The Wailers album.

I had an elder sister, Fiona. I have her still. As children, we would literally try to tear pieces out of one another. As adults, we could hardly be more dissimilar. I am slim and gregarious and clever with words, while she has always been bulky and reclusive and can't write a grammatical sentence. (Which isn't to say that she is without talent – in fact, she is a wonderful sketcher and painter.) I look rather like my dad, Fiona very much more like our Scottish-born mum, who had to leave school at fourteen to work in a munitions factory, but who is as clever a person as I've ever met, a gifted and prolific poet.

At eight, I hoped that Paul McCartney might come to adore me as I adored him, but within a year or so I had thrown him over for Mickey Dolenz of the Monkees. In anticipation of our inevitable betrothal, I practised writing Claire Dolenz in my school notebook. (Now it can be told: Mistress's real name is Claire.) My parents were nonetheless informed early on that I had an IQ of 148. There have been many times over the years since when I have wished my creditors would accept that in lieu of sterling.

Eighteen endless, excruciating months after Douglas Hughson pronounced me the Mouse, Mum, for whom the rot had set in with Elvis, discovered herself emotionally disinclined to deal with her daughter idolising a flame-haired wannabe alien of indeterminable gender. As she watched my transformation from obedient wallflower into defiantly gaudy Ziggy Stardust lookalike, her concern increased almost hourly. When, finally able to endure no more, she burst into my purple bedroom and began to remove all the photos of David Bowie I'd lovingly affixed to the wall, I realised that my life was finally proceeding exactly as I'd come to hope.

But for Bowie, I probably would have remained a dutiful daughter of the suburbs, married a bloke as plain and hopeless as I was, had 2.2 children, and died of boredom a few weeks short of my thirty-fourth birthday. But then, a few weeks shy of my fourteenth, I sat down in front of the TV to watch *Top of the Pops*. As the camera cut from Jimmy Savile to the gorgeously decadent Mr Bowie, his arm draped casually around Mick Ronson, I felt a distinct and never-before-experienced sensation in my loins. David Cassidy and Donny Osmond had left me cold. The Bay City Rollers inspired derision. But here . . . *here* was my Waterloo. As Bowie posed and postured through 'Starman', I could hardly contain the hormonal maelstrom. Suddenly I dared to imagine a rather more interesting future for myself.

I joined the David Bowie Fan Club in late 1972, and greeted its every mailing as it fell through my letterbox with the same delight and excitement as a telegram from Her Majesty. On an otherwise ordinary school morning, I found one of the club's envelopes on the mat, tore it open, and discovered that I might win tickets to see David perform the 1980 Floor Show at the Marquee for American television. All I had to do was paint or draw one of the six best portraits of the great man, who would himself choose the winners. I almost went into a faint at the thought.

To say that winning a ticket was a matter of life or death was understating its importance.

I disappeared into my bedroom, not to be glimpsed again for days. To say that I worked feverishly would be to suggest that I was very much more casual than was actually the case. My parents tapped periodically on the door to check that I was still alive. In fact, I had never been *more* alive! The trusty and by now far-too-small desk my parents had bought me for my tenth birthday creaked under the onslaught of my attempts to capture His essence. I discarded effort after effort until at last I knew that the endless hours spent drawing hundreds of David Bowies all over my school books had paid off. A head and shoulders colour portrait in soft pencil took shape.

I could do no better. I posted it off, praying in every idle moment that it would find favour.

Six weeks passed. Glacially. Then one morning, as I packed my school bag, another brown envelope slipped through the door. My hands trembled. My heart rate increased precipitously. My mouth was the Sahara. It seemed to take six weeks just to tear the envelope open.

A ticket to the show.

I momentarily forgot how to breathe. I was going to swoon.

My parents were rather less ecstatic. Did I know where 100 Wardour Street was? If so, was I aware that Soho was absolutely crawling with women of ill repute, opium dens, swarthy, scarred lowlifes who would casually make a meal of an innocent such as myself? They agonised about my solo flight into the Abyss, but quite correctly surmised that withholding their permission might prove fatal. I could go, they finally decreed through clenched teeth, provided I came back out to my waiting father at an hour befitting a girl expected at Ealing Grammar School at 8:45 the following morning.

I was hysterical with excitement the night my dad, a man of few words – and fewer still at the prospect of his younger daughter's imminent corruption – accompanied me to Wardour

Street, London W1. On the inbound train, we ran again and again and again through the drill. I was to meet him outside at exactly 10 p.m. so he could see me safely home. Never mind that the show wouldn't finish until 11.

I joined the queue behind two worldly young beauties in identical tights, each with one red leg and one black. They might have been eighteen, and their conversation oozed sophistication.

'We gotta get in, Sharon,' one muttered vehemently to the other.

'I know,' Sharon agreed. 'We just gotta!'

They looked at me, and at the ticket I held with all my might. They'd have had to kill me first.

I was twelve miles from home, but felt a thousand, a stranger in a strange land. For the first time (of several million), I stood on the soggy beer-soaked carpet of the Marquee, sweating in the heat with fast-beating heart, reeling from the alien sights, smells, and sounds, from the unprecedented thrill of it all. There was the Andy Warhol superstar Cherry Vanilla! There David's American publicist, Leee Black Childers. And there, in a corner, Angela Bowie with three-year-old Zowie Bowie, the fruit of my hero's loins.

Sharon and her mate had got in somehow. Presumably trying to curry favour, they approached the Bowie progeny. 'Hello, darling,' one of them cooed, a little patronisingly, I thought.

'Fuck off,' the wee Zowie suggested brightly, and everyone revelled in his precocity.

A camera ran over my foot but I felt no pain, for there, a

mere four feet from me – near enough to touch if I lunged – was Himself. He looked at me! And I, shivering with embarrassment, averted my eyes.

He performed. I watched in adoration. Others performed. Marianne Faithfull, dressed as a nun! The Troggs!

My father!

I looked, panic-stricken, at my watch – 10:15! The show was far from over, but my dad was guaranteed to be pacing anxiously outside, growing increasingly irate with every step. Cinderella had no choice but to flee the ball. One day soon, though, she'd stay all night.

Having no trace of shame, I entered a competition to be named David Bowie's Superfan. The competition involved writing in and explaining, in twenty-five words or fewer, why I deserved that coveted title. I got my mum, a gifted writer in her own right, to supply an affidavit substantiating my claim. And then they gave the award to some vile Welsh git called Simon Whosit. Apoplectic with righteous indignation, I wrote him a letter – advising that, regardless of what the contest's idiot judges thought, it was I who deserved the crown he wore – and was flabbergasted, mere days later, when I received a letter back from him, one that didn't suggest that I go play blindfolded on the motorway, but tried its best to comfort and reassure me.

We began, of course, to correspond. I learned that he was a designer and puppetmaster at a theatre in Wales, and that every time Bowie changed his image, he, at considerable expense, changed his own. He confided that his mother was ashamed of him because of his effeminacy. Be still, my heart, I thought, and invited him to London.

He hadn't been exaggerating. What a tiny, delicate thing, albeit at least 40 per cent nose! We headed immediately for the West End, there to pose up a storm in our Thin White Duke jumpsuits. I took him home to meet Mum. In he traipsed with his upswept flame-coloured hair, earring, varnished fingernails, and shoulder bag. Down plummeted Mum's jaw. I found out later that, as we retired to my bedroom to listen to our favourite tracks, Mum burst so hard into laughter that she uprooted the fern she'd been tending on the windowsill.

I was pretty sure I could learn to ignore Simon's remarkable hooter, but it turned out that he was reluctant to leave Wales, as he'd long fancied a career in coal mining.

I joke.

Resplendent – no, absolutely luminous! – in bright yellow satin Oxford bags, green satin shirt, red platform boots, and *de rigueur* solitary diamante earring, my newly feather-cut hair an intriguing new colour thanks to the Hint of a Tint I'd used over Mum's dead body, I was the epitome of what the press enjoyed calling a Bowie Victim. And Mum died a thousand deaths as I headed for Oxford Street, intent on buying the very first copy of *Aladdin Sane*, released that very morning. Net curtains twitched furiously as I ambled to my comparably chic friend Susan's. Riding together on the tube into the West End, we revelled in the raised eyebrows of our fellow passengers. Let them gape! Our fingers were firmly on The Pulse. And my evolution from the plain little Mouse of my wretched early teens into a glamorous, exotic, and – let it be said! – sultry creature unmistakably destined for great adventures was complete.

As the train hurtled into the tunnel at Finchley Road, Susan drew a gold circle on my forehead much like the one Himself had sported on his Ziggy Stardust tour. Strutting confidently into the HMV shop in Oxford Street, we found ourselves surrounded by *Aladdin Sane* album covers from floor to ceiling. And on every last one, there was a lightning bolt across the Bowie visage – no trace of a golden orb. We gasped simultaneously in dismay. Already out of date!

My confidence increased nonetheless, as too did my appetite for self-expression. I became friends with Jill, a wannabe film star classmate who shared my Bowie fixation. She had been allowed to paint her bedroom midnight blue with gold stars on the ceiling, and I was green with envy. Aching to become part of her crowd, I dutifully attended the symposia of pompous young thespians-to-be that she hosted in her astonishing room. She implored me to join the Young Theatre, a local group already attended by several names who would become gigantic years hence. (If I mentioned Dame Judith Dench, Kenneth Branagh, Ralph Fiennes, Sir Anthony Hopkins, Gary Oldman, Elizabeth Hurley, and the late Sir Laurence Olivier, would you know that none of them had any connection whatever to the Young Theatre?) I demurred. She dangled in front of me a luscious blond carrot called Brian, after whom she knew I lusted. Brian, she casually observed, wanted to train at RADA and become an actor. Acting suddenly became very much more interesting to me.

*   *   *

I sat shivering in the old church hall in North Harrow, waiting to audition for a part in the Young Theatre's next production. 'Run!' the Mouse implored in my mind's ear. 'Scurry to safety before you make a perfect tit of yourself!'

'Watch yer mouth,' growled I, and, hardly able to believe what I was doing, got up on stage when my name was called and read lines, a staggering feat of heroism. (No infantryman charged with taking out a German machine gunner in the Battle of the Bulge had had to overcome greater terror.)

They liked me, and Brian the luscious carrot shot me admiring glances. I was offered a big part, that of the bedridden Mum, and Brian the luscious carrot asked me out. I was beside myself with pleasure – and dread. At some point in the foreseeable future I would have to perform before a whole auditoriumful of living Britons.

We rehearsed and rehearsed and rehearsed. And rehearsed. While most of my peers couldn't wait to be old enough for such adult recreations as getting one another pregnant, I wanted time to stand still. It waits for neither man nor apprehensive teen actress, though, and opening night insisted eventually on arriving. I took my place on stage in bed, where my character spent most of her time. 'Run!' the Mouse shrieked hysterically. I was too weak with dread to reply. As the curtains opened, I prayed for the ground to do the same, but then something extraordinary happened. I heard myself delivering my lines pretty nearly flawlessly over the beating of my own heart. I was transformed. That was no terrified schoolgirl from Ruislip on stage, but a sullen middle-aged Northern widow. God, was it glorious!

Brian the luscious carrot concurred. He bought Bowie's *Pin-Ups* and invited me round to listen to it in his bedroom. The critic from the Harrow *Observer* concurred, describing me as 'very good indeed', if failing to invite me over. I could have set a new British indoor record for gloating. There was no trace of the Mouse anywhere.

I needed a starring vehicle, and if the Young Theatre wouldn't provide it, then I would damn well provide my own. I went to the original cast production of *The Rocky Horror Show* in Chelsea. By the time I was back out on the Kings Road pavement, I had resolved to write a version of my own based on, let's see . . . well, why not *King Lear*, which I was very much enjoying studying for A level?

My teachers were aghast. Emergency conferences were called and hard questions asked about my lyrics, none thornier than that regarding the possible obsceneness of (younger readers, avert your eyes!) *coxcomb*. I was notorious, nothing less than A Controversial Figure! God, did I love it.

As reimagined by me, *King Lear* became a revue. The Bard spun in his grave and then, seeing that mere spinning wouldn't suffice, climbed creakily from the crypt and ran stiffly through the streets of Stratford-upon-Avon pleading with the locals to alert the authorities down in Harrow. We would not be deterred, however, not as long as my heretofore contemptuous classmates gaped in wonderment as we rehearsed during lunch hours, before bigger and bigger crowds.

My Ealing Grammar School classmates had always sought me out, but now they were doing so to invite me to A-list parties, rather than to humiliate me. I often went with my best friend,

Judi, whom my mum had dubbed the Elephant Girl after her maiden ascent of our stairs induced countless ornaments to topple over in submission and shatter. I liked her being very much less svelte than I, very much less attractive. (I was an awful person. I admit it. You were an awful person at that age yourself.) The most popular boys in the class commonly remembered business that required them to walk down the halls in the same direction I was going.

My clothes and makeup became ever more outrageous. I became quite the *provocateuse*. In English Literature class, we sprayed Judi's lemon perfume over the unfortunate boy in front of us, and he was grateful for our attention. I never dreamed that, decades hence, managing directors would pay me to spray perfume on them and impugn their heterosexuality. We passed one another long, lurid notes about what we might wear to the next party. Who you callin' Mouse?

My turquoise mohair tank top and satin trousers drew the eye of Graham Bolton, one of the alpha males in the year above mine. I was incredibly flattered, and for fear he'd transfer his attention elsewhere, didn't play hard to get, allowing him to snog me under the beverages table at a party.

Behold, I had my first Proper Boyfriend.

Within ten minutes of meeting him, my mum had annointed him. The Son I'd Have Loved to Have Had and my beaming dad was pumping his hand like a man possessed.

When my family and I went on holiday in Cornwall, Graham would write every day to tell me how much he missed me, often enclosing photographs of Bowie he'd clipped from magazines. Every day after school, he'd wait for me in his Afghan coat to drive me home in his blue Mini while '21st Century Schizoid Man' blared from his eight-track. Our song!

I gave him my virginity atop his parents' double bed one night while Black Sabbath bleated and rumbled malevolently on the stereo. If memory serves, his parents weren't in the bed at the time, but his mum soon sussed what was going on and sent me to the local clinic for The Pill. She and Graham's dad invited my own folks to Graham's huge eighteenth birthday party. To my absolute astonishment – my folks never mingled with anyone outside the family, *ever* – they came, and Mum cut the rug with Graham's dad. Eighteen months later, to the limitless delight of all concerned, we were engaged.

Could life have been sweeter?

Well, yes. At the end-of-term concert, my little revue savoured what might generously have been called an ambiguous reception, and I realised I'd misread my classmates' earlier wonderment. But I would transform their dubious or even pained expressions into ecstatic grins! I formed a permanent band, recruiting an unlikely cast of thousands from among my sixth-form classmates. Not just anyone was welcome, mind you – those unable to fog a mirror were right out. The final line-up – and what a long line it was! – included a left-handed drummer with two right feet, a classical pianist, a bass player so slender that if he turned sideways you couldn't see him, a saxophonist who spat and dribbled alarmingly, and no fewer than five lead guitarists, each of whom sounded as though he were playing in boxing gloves. I called it Lear, of course, and blagged us a spot at my local between sets by the lukewarm resident jazz trio.

Oh, what a set we performed, comprising favourites from the very cream of post-Beatles British rock acts – Pink Floyd's 'Money', Led Zeppelin's 'Rock and Roll', even Himself's haunting 'Space Oddity' – some of them very nearly recognisable. And then there were the originals, also intermittently identifiable as Western music.

There was nothing ambiguous about the looks on the faces of *this* audience. This audience's horror was palpable. Poor Graham, dutifully in attendance to capture the moment on magnetic tape, gently suggested that I explore alternative expressive outlets. 'Told you so,' piped up the Mouse. 'You've done it now, haven't you?'

Little did she realise that, without knowing it, Lear had ushered in the punk era. And oh, was my stock about to rise.

CHAPTER FOUR

Punks Overrun Chiswick – Thousands Flee!

I took my three A levels, high IQ, and engaging personality out into the world, and with them got a job at a West End advertising agency. My first week at Shackle, Hammer & Tongs was a real eye-opener. Indeed, my pretty hazel eyes felt at times as though they might bulge right out of my head as I typed promotional budgets for TV and print campaigns. Surely there were too many zeroes at the end! Could it really be that agencies spent ten times more on one little campaign for some naff new brand of breath mint than my poor dad earned in a year's fruiterering?

A week after I started, the creative department, being

British, and thus ever on the lookout for excuses to get legless, took me out for a welcoming drink. I was a nineteen-year-old fruiterer's daughter and had to that point drunk only halves of lager and lime with Graham, a man of limited means. Seeing my eagerness to explore the exciting new world of alcoholism with which many of them were apparently intimately acquainted, the creatives, as they were known round the agency, told me to order whatever I fancied. I fancied gin. And vodka. And wines of different hues and vintages. And exotic cocktails with little umbrellas protruding from them.

In a very short while, I was very much the life and soul of the party, seeing which, my boss, Ed, took me aside (no easy undertaking, given the fact that someone had apparently rewritten most of the major laws of physics since I'd arrived at the pub) and eagerly confided that he'd had a succession of wet dreams about me over the preceding week. 'Not to worry, Eddie baby,' I assured him, albeit not entirely intelligibly. 'How much can a couple of towels cost?' Whereupon I absolutely howled with laughter and apparently cured Ed's problem, about which I never heard another syllable.

I got back to our table, had a wee one for the road, staggered back to Baker Street tube station – knocking over four motorcycles, three apple carts, two fellow drunks, and a partridge in a pear tree en route – miraculously boarded the right train home, got back to my boyfriend Graham's parents' place, and spent the balance of the evening vomiting.

Ah, yoof.

When I awoke the following morning, I was surprised to discover that work had apparently begun during the night on installing a new British Rail station in the middle of my cerebrum, but nevertheless made it to my office, and by mid-afternoon was able to endure the clamour of someone whispering into a telephone at the other end of the building. Shackle's creative director, who seemed to want to get very well acquainted indeed, came over and showed me the promotional sticker he'd designed for my group Wildside, which I am horrified to realise I haven't yet told you about.

I hadn't, as you'd hoped, packed in my dreams of a career as a pop diva after Lear's remarkable debut and farewell gig. Indeed, within mere weeks of Lear's disintegration, for the usual 'creative differences', I answered an ad that a big lumbering bass player and his guitarist mate had placed in the *Melody Maker* for a girl singer, and got the job, although in truth there was very little job to get. After several weeks' rehearsal, I finally summoned the nerve to suggest that we try to add a drummer and lead guitarist. The others thought this a brilliant idea, and we auditioned several candidates in the death-trap basement in south London where it was our curse to rehearse.

Two of them were the Giuliano brothers from Edinburgh, drummer Paolo and guitarist Martin, the former a suave older man of twenty-six. We took one look at one another and got wet and hard, respectively. They joined the band and I took to wearing the same ugly denim clothing they did, as this was the era of pub rock and I, the fervent Bowiephile, hadn't the courage to cry, 'But this is *wrong*!' When we took breaks from rehearsals, the suave elder Giuliano took me aside and made clear that he hoped *we* might get very well acquainted indeed – an ambition that I avidly shared.

He took me and Julie, a woman he'd been seeing, to the Red Cow in Hammersmith to witness one of the first public performances of the Stranglers. When Julie got bored and went home prematurely, Paolo and I literally ran out to his van, both trembling to unleash the lust by which we were both consumed. A passer-by couldn't have been blamed for imagining that the Welsh national rugby team was practising within.

Poor Graham. Instead of spending my weekends with him, I was now 'rehearsing' with Wildside. I would dutifully call him from wherever I was, hear the hurt in his voice as I related that I wouldn't be home in time to see him that night, and still stay out. But how could good old dependable twenty-year-old Graham compete with an exciting, worldly older man with an exotic name like Paolo? Did he honestly imagine that I, the nineteen-year-old *femme fatale*, would prefer sipping lager and lime in North Harrow to taking acid with Paolo in romantic Stockwell and listening to the new Tubes album?

Back in Ruislip, both my family and poor Graham's were in agony, trying to figure out what could have come over me. 'You're using our house like lodgings!' Mum wailed, quite correctly. Well, if you don't fancy it, I thought, I'll go elsewhere. I rented the microscopic bedsit beneath Wildside's big lumbering bass player's digs in Chiswick – and then grew ever more distraught as the day I would have to tell my parents loomed nearer and nearer. Making my way home on the tube from my new job as receptionist in a film production company in Wardour Street, I hurled myself from the carriage to throw up on the station platform.

When finally, with only twenty-four hours to go before I took over the bedsit, I worked up the nerve to announce what I'd done, the shock on Mum's and Dad's faces was painful to see, and I felt the lowest form of life. But their love was unconditional. They not only helped me move, but gave me an alarm clock and new saucepans. Just before they left, my Dad took me aside – no modest feat in my LP-cover-sized first home-away-from-home – and assured me that if I wanted to have Sunday lunch with them the next day, I would be welcome. There were tears in my mother's eyes as she kissed me goodbye.

One night Paolo happened to glance out of his window in the nick of time to see his purportedly former girlfriend Julie coming up the street, and he unceremoniously shoved me out of the back door while she swaggered in the front. Take that, little *femme fatale*. I could barely find my way to the tube station for my blinding tears. Just as I was about to board a northbound train, my two-faced little knight in shining armour grabbed me from behind. Julie was gone for ever, he assured me, and he couldn't bear the thought of even a single night without me.

It turned out that she'd only gone on holiday.

The nineteen-year-old *femme fatale* became a nineteen-year-old basket case. Every time Paolo took me to a club, a woman other than myself seemed to catch my adored's eye. He would excuse himself to visit the Gents and I would sit there and sit there and sit there while everyone else on the premises sniggered behind their hands. *Look at the gullible little cow, imagining her boyfriend's thirty-five minutes in the loo!* By and by, I would be able to bear no more, and would go looking for him, invariably finding him with his tongue halfway down some slut's throat.

I cajoled. I wept. I raged. I howled. I sulked. I threatened. And the man I loved womanised blithely on.

In too much pain to think clearly, I sought consolation in the slender white arms of his brother Martin, the guitar player, who was soon drafted into You've Doubtless Heard of Them, and Probably Even Own Several of Their Recordings, As They Were Enormous, But My Lawyers Have Advised Me Not to Identify Them for Fear of an Expensive, Debilitating Libel Suit (hereafter called Doubtless). The product of a patriarchal society, I so fancied the idea of being a famous guitarist's girlfriend that I didn't evict him, even when he announced that he preferred wanking to making love to me. In retrospect, I recognise that I may have had some self-esteem issues.

Doubtless went on a tour of Europe, and I went to Hamburg with them. The piano player's long-suffering girlfriend and I would stand outside their dressing-room door and beat into unconsciousness any predatory little Kraut tart who seemed to fancy either of our men. I witnessed first-hand the altogether shocking behaviour of the modern British rock musician on tour abroad. In Seattle, I saw the band cram a small mud shark up a girl's fanny. Or maybe that was something I read about Led Zeppelin. Or Hear'Say. I was putting a great deal of cocaine up my little sniffer, and my memories are less exact than they might be.

Once home, I realised that I could no longer pretend to be satisfied with the services available to David Bowie fans in this, the country of my birth. I'd joined his official fan club, and had even come to correspond with the wacky sisters who ran the Bowie Appreciation Society from a cave in the Isle of Wight. But as he became ever more enormous, the devoted, incompetent fans who'd long run the fan club were supplanted by Major Fulfillment, an enormous corporation that looked after lots of megastars' fan mail – and did a damned rotten job of it. My friend Colin and I decided that the great man's British fans deserved much better, wrote some promotional material, and put an ad in the *Melody Maker*.

Instant success.

The floor of my little bedsit disappeared under paperwork. Our membership leapt from eighty to 379 to over a thousand. The postman, who had back problems, hated me. And still they came, attracted by the fact that, with our remarkable grapevine and friendship with Bowie's ex-manager Ken Pitt, we were able to disseminate the freshest possible goss on our mutual idol. By the time he released *Heroes*, British Bowie fans had come to regard us with something closely resembling reverence. After one of his performances at Wembley, we threw a gigantic party in the West End where we played rare out-takes and showed even rarer film clips. The ranks of our membership grew even more swollen. Bowie's manager's lawyers sent us a threatening letter. Ken Pitt suggested that we ignore it, and we were pleased to oblige.

When Martin came home to Chiswick, I surreptitiously searched his suitcase for clues that he'd been unfaithful. (Hang on, you're thinking. How could he be unfaithful to a woman with whom he wasn't actually having a carnal relationship? Do shut up, I reply.) I found them. He'd had a Swede, a blonde Swede, albeit not the one in Abba. I was devastated. He was barely apologetic. We parted. I noted with relief that there were no more Giuliano brothers to break my heart.

What went around came around. He moved to New York, and his first week there was mugged in the subway and relieved of his guitar.

Punk supplanted pub rock. I wore much more interesting clothing, but removed it all – or at least the most important bits – with pretty scant encouragement. Such were the times. I was theoretically the girlfriend now of a principal contributor to a leading punk magazine that my lawyers think I ought not to mention, but he was commonly self-medicated to the point of being of little use to a lusty twenty-year-old. So, four or five nights a week I would take a cab from the Vortex in Wardour Street or the Roxy in Covent Garden to some real or self-described punk luminary's squalid squat, there to wake up the next morning with only the vaguest memory of the previous night's debauchery. I have reason to believe that I gained carnal knowledge of both Joe Strummer of the Clash and Jean-Jacques Burnel of the Stranglers. I ingested much speed to get me through the workday, and undoubtedly did irreparable harm to my central nervous system.

I nearly got run out of Chiswick by a mob of irate local peasants with pitchforks after a party I threw in my little bedsit got completely out of control. I'd handed out invitations at all the best unspeakable punk dives, and apparently everyone who'd got one had invited 250 of his or her closest friends. It made the papers. And when the landlady turned up the next afternoon to collect the rent, and beheld carnage that sniggered at any hope of adequate description – splintered banisters, smashed windows, debauched virgins, bloody bodies in the storm drains, neighbours' gardens drowning beneath small lakes of punk urine – she was not to be mollified to learn that some of it was Billy Idol, Jimmy (Sham 69) Purcey, Gaye Advert and Poly (X-Ray Specs) Styrene's. 'Pay two months' rent in compensation,' she sobbed bitterly, 'or be gone.' I paid, and stayed.

Ah, yoof.

A girl had two choices in those days. She could devote her Saturday afternoons to strolling down the King's Road, seeing and being seen in Boy and Sex and the market, or she could have tattooed on her forehead *I'm a gormless loser without even the most rudimentary sense of how to spend my leisure time*. I chose the former.

My partner in crime was Mandy, another dutiful daughter of the suburbs. We'd somehow noticed each other one night at the Marquee through the thick cigarette smoke, spilled lager puddles, and clouds of evaporating perspiration, and sat down together.

'I feel a bit of a prat,' I admitted, at the top of my lungs. If one hoped to be heard over the band, one bellowed.

'But why?' she shouted.

'No safety pins,' I screamed. 'No rips. No unsightly stains. One feels so overdressed.'

She gaped. 'You know,' she shrieked, 'I feel exactly the same.' The whole audience turned to frown at us. The band had stopped, in that abrupt way that was so fashionable in those days, as though someone had turned off their power between 'exactly' and 'same'.

In any event, we agreed to meet the following evening and buy ourselves some proper punk gear – and discovered, when we did so, that it cost rather more than we'd expected not to look overdressed. For a Marks & Sparks T-shirt they'd got someone to throw-up on, and whose arms they'd ripped off and then reattached with safety pins of the sort you could buy fifty of at Woolworth's for £1.49, Sex wanted £25.

'Why, we could probably make our own!' Mandy exclaimed excitedly, inspiring the shop boy to sneer contemptuously.

'Yes,' I agreed, 'but it just wouldn't be the same, would it?' I was being ironic.

We repaired to Mandy's extremely middle-class suburban home to desecrate old clothing her mum had earmarked for delivery to Oxfam. But on Saturday, when we were to convene and display our handiwork to one another, the Bowie fan in me gained the upper hand and chose skintight black satin jeans, sparkly Union Jack socks, and transparent plastic stilettos to go with my £18.50 Sex Pistols T-shirt, two-tone burgundy and red hair, and black panda eyes. I made up for it by thinking to buy a dog collar and lead at the pet shop just outside my local tube station. I put them on the not-entirely-sold-on-the-idea Mandy when we met in Sloane Square, and off we went, our very appearance giving two fingers to stodgy British propriety, to the gross inequities of the secondary modern, to the class system in general.

In those days, you could barely get out of the tube for all the well-scrubbed suburban kids posing as punks and American tourists gaping in horror at them through the viewfinders of their cameras. We immediately caught the eye of some Americans.

'Oh, my Lord, Brad. That panda-eyed girl's black satin jeans are . . . *skintight*!'

Click. Click. Click.

'And her hair! Two different colours! Or, as we'd say back home, colors!'

Click. Click. Click.

'And the one is leading the other on a leash, Brad! The other members of the Ladies Auxiliary won't believe their ears!'

Click. Click. Click.

We must have been doing something right, or he must have had a transparent shoe fetish, because one of the photographers the European press had dispatched to chronicle the odd spectacle of well-scrubbed suburban kids posing as punks for horrified American tourists stayed right in front of us, clicking away madly, as we proceeded towards World's End. We felt such film stars! But we were dutiful daughters of the suburbs, with a sense of fair play deep in our genes, and dutifully struck all the poses we'd learned from *The Punk Poseur's Handbook*.

Weeks passed. Day after day after day, excluding weekends of course, I reported exactly on time, and often even a few minutes early, to the Musicians' Union, where I was now working. Somewhere in the world, famous people died. Elsewhere, babies were born.

And then the deluge, on an otherwise quiet Sunday, when I surprised my mum with a visit home. Ordinarily her face would have turned into pure gentle sunshine on encountering her younger daughter outside Londis, but not today. Today, a thundercloud. 'How *could* you?' she wailed.

How could I what, exactly?

She pulled the *Observer*'s colour supplement from her bag and let it fall, too filthy to touch, to the pavement. Doing its part, it fell open to a double-page spread about punk, and how it was destroying British youth. And how better to illustrate this woeful state of affairs than with a photo of a little panda-eyed slut leading a shameless tart on a dog lead? There was no anguish anywhere else in the universe at that moment. It was all in my mum's face and voice. 'How *could* you?' she asked again. 'What will people *think*?' And with that, she spun on her heel and hurried off to spare me the sight of her bursting into tears.

How very proud of myself I felt at that moment.

And no end in sight. The photos had apparently gone into some sort of library (leave it to me to attract the attention of the best photographer in the crowd!), and showed up for months afterwards in different publications, including French *Elle* and *Traditional Crochet*.

I looked for a band that needed a girl singer, and found one, the Swords, in the *Melody Maker*. I made an appointment to meet the bass player in Wardour Street. He turned out to be tubby and to be wearing two-years-ago's velvet jacket, with a Rupert Bear badge on the lapel. I briefly considered pretending not to be the person he'd spoken to on the phone, but here he came, grinning delightedly. He was gratifyingly enchanted by every syllable out of my mouth, and I agreed to audition for them. After insisting that they replace the drummer, I signed on as their Deborah Harry surrogate. Looking back, I am unable to explain why I didn't also insist that the rhythm guitarist be forbidden to wear the four-sizes-too-small school blazer in which he fancied himself to be so wonderfully reminiscent of Dr Feelgood's Wilko Johnson, but the attentive reader will remember that I was suffering in those days from severe sleep deprivation.

And to be honest, I was no great fashionplate myself. Having not yet realised that Sex Sells, or at least not having wrapped my synapses around the idea of selling it myself, I wore a boys' school uniform and a loosened necktie both on stage and in our publicity photo. We changed our name to the Voyeurs, cut a demo of a brazen Blondie knockoff called 'Front Row Boy' that a formerly eminent American rock critic would later pronounce ten times better than all my subsequent musician boyfriends' tapes put together, and supported Eddie & The Hot Rods at the Hope and Anchor. I got sacked because I was too depressed about Martin Giuliano's infidelity to attend rehearsals.

With my departure, New Wave inevitably soon found itself a comfortable place in the musty room where discredited pop music styles go to languish in ignominy until the children of their original adherents rediscover them and regard them for four or five days – or until they realise that their mums and dads used to like them, whichever comes first – as 'cool'. I was delighted when it got supplanted by the New Romantics, as I could relate in a big, big way to the ridiculous costuming and immoderate makeup. I became a regular at the Blitz in Covent Garden, into which door, er, men Steve Strange and Boy George allowed only the most exotic and fetching. I was never turned away. I also allowed myself to be glimpsed on a regular basis at Billy's, later renamed Gossips, where the exotic and fetching met to pretend to be painfully bored with one another and to twitch in some vague semblance of rhythm to the wilfully twee sounds of Kraftwerk and Soft Cell.

'Twas in the latter venue that I caught the eye (among other body parts) of a tall, pretty boy with a fantastic cleft chin who was soon to be hired as drummer in a New Romantic group you're even more sure to have heard of than Doubtless.

Unable to endure the memory of Martin Giuliano masturbating energetically beside me within its narrow confines, I abandoned the Chiswick bedsit for one in Hounslow, just at the end of Heathrow's Runway 4. The New Romantic drummer's dick turned out to be strangely scimitar-shaped, and consequently not entirely comfortable, so I was grateful for the diversion of occasional Qantas and Air New Zealand 747s landing on the roof.

Things weren't good at home. My dad's business had been suffering terribly since Tesco came to town with its remarkable selection and low prices. 'I should bloody well hope they'd be low,' Dad groused. 'On a typical weekday, I'll buy twenty heads of iceberg lettuce. They'll probably buy 200. But is somebody there going to help you pick out the best one, like I do? I don't bloody think so.' At the rate he was going, he figured that he'd be able to stay in business a maximum of six more months.

He said that a guy from Tesco had been round to see him about a job. The guy had flattered my dad a treat, saying that Tesco very much needed a person with his superior knowledge and appreciation of fruit and veg to help make their grocery section the best in the borough. 'But I've worked for myself my whole adult life,' my dad brooded. 'I don't have the slightest interest in becoming a cog in some huge bloody corporate machine, not the slightest.'

Every Tuesday evening, I would head, lavishly made up and outlandishly costumed, for the Blitz to perpetuate my standing as a major New Romantic face. I would do the peculiar and preposterous dance – throwing both arms down to the left while kicking the left leg up to the right, and then hopping – that was so fashionable among us New Romantics, or would simply accept the flattery of those awed by my co-proprietorship of Subterraneans. This group included a pair of staggeringly gorgeous Amazon sisters who brought to my birthday party a shy, pale, slightly podgy male friend, Gary, without whom they'd have looked very much more striking. I was embarrassed and dismayed to learn through the grapevine that this personage had been smitten with me. A couple of weeks thereafter, though, when I found myself standing beside him at the bar of the Blitz, I realised he wasn't the disaster I'd originally thought. He seemed to have dropped half a stone and to have invested in some black eyeliner, which he wore well, and he asked me out. I accepted, but decided on the night to suffer a frightful outbreak of German measles instead. Gazza consoled himself by going on to become the toast of several continents and the odd large island as Gary Numan, of 'Are "Friends" Electric?' and 'Cars' fame.

I recovered from my fateful illness and hurried back to the Blitz, there to prop up one of the walls with Billy Currie's long-suffering girlfriend – and there also, much more importantly, to espy against the opposite wall a guy popularly known as Tchaikovsky, the guitarist in Doubtless's little sister band, known for its Alice Cooperesque hi-jinks on stage. I'd glimpsed him at the Ship, but understood him to be insufferably arrogant, and thus was apprehensive when I saw that he was weaving his way towards me, a half-empty bottle of wine in hand.

'Let's make,' I said, or would have had I been a character in a 1950s American sitcom, 'like a banana and split.' But my mate Julie fancied Tchaikovsky's, so we stood our ground. He turned out to be as arrogant as advertised, but also witty and good-looking – sort of Julian Cope crossed with Peter Perrett of the Only Ones, but better than either. He'd just signed a deal with RCA and would I like to come and see his etchings – no, hold on . . . listen to his demos? I would, as it turned out, as the squat he shared with three radical lesbian feminists (don't ask – I didn't) was only a short taxi ride away in Bethnal Green.

I liked his tapes, and stayed the night – chastely, as he passed out from drunkenness. As he did on our second and third nights together too. A young woman less blinded by love might have detected a pattern. Finally, on the fourth night, we consummated our attraction to one another. He told me that his father had once been imprisoned on the Gulag Archipelago, but was now an acclaimed chef, and that his mother, a lapsed gypsy, had helped his father welcome most of the Big Names in European Cooking to their home. I found him an irresistible combination of intelligence, beauty, and danger, and wound up spending seven straight nights with him, growing so besotted over their course that I neglected to tell anyone where I was. My friends were beside themselves with worry.

On the seventh night, we went to the Rock Garden in Covent Garden and were several drinks down when Todd Rundgren's 'Love Is the Answer' began to play. Suddenly Tchaikovsky put his head on the table, covered it with his arms, and began to sob, quite inconsolably. I didn't know quite how – or even if – to console him. I finally put my hand on his arm and asked if I could help, but received no response. He was all alone in the universe with his agony. At last I got up and walked out. He didn't follow.

I could barely function at work the next day, worrying about him, but knew neither his real name nor his phone number. It occurred to me that he'd mentioned his manager's name at one point. For hours, I tried to remember it, here concentrating with all my might, there being very nonchalant, trying to trick my mind into believing I'd lost interest.

Bob Biggerstaff.

Bob was very suspicious when I rang, but eventually agreed to inform my mercurial new love of my concern. He rang back. It had been the first anniversary of his father's suicide, and he'd been overwhelmed thinking about it. His name was Vladimir. I was not to call him Vlad.

We went to Paris together, and capitalised on the fact that, if you'd had very poor eyesight and glimpsed him across the width of a very wide, dimly lit, smoke-filled restaurant, you might, if very drunk, have mistaken Vladimir for Keith Richards, who owned a flat near where we stayed. A local hotelier put us up free, and fed us at the nearby bistro he also owned. And when we sat on the steps of Sacré Coeur and someone handed Vladimir a guitar, a huge crowd formed within ten minutes, as word that the Rolling Stones were doing an impromptu acoustic gig spread like wildfire through the various *arrondissements*, as the French enjoy calling their neighbourhoods. When we returned to London, I got a job at ITV as a copy executive, vetting TV and radio ads, and a tiny flat in Belsize Park, into which Vladimir moved with me.

The news at home was that, after twenty-two years in the same convenient location, Mansfield Fruit & Veg had closed its doors. After he and my mum got back from a week's holiday, the first he'd taken in centuries, on the Isle of Wight, my dad would start work as First Assistant Manager of the grocery section at the gigantic Tesco in Harrow. I was heartbroken for him, but he wouldn't have it. 'Mustn't be *should*y,' he explained bravely. 'It *should* be possible for an independent greengrocer to stay in business even after the big chains move into the neighbourhood, but I'm satisfied that it isn't – or at least it wasn't for me. Which leaves me with a choice. I can torture myself with what *should* be, or learn to be as happy as I can with what is. I choose the latter. And let that be a lesson to you, love.' For perhaps the second time in my life, I saw tears in my dad's eyes, but they may well have been tears of love, as the tears that spilled from my own were.

*   *   *

My ITV salary wasn't sufficient to support Vladimir's appetite for Dom Perignon (or, frankly, anything else containing alcohol) and controlled substances; and spending time at an actual income-producing job while he could be manifesting his genius was inconceivable to him. It turned out, too, that the fine folks at my bank had far greater interest in my overdraft than in his brilliance. I had to do something, and quick.

I'd long been intrigued by the *Evening Standard*'s classified ads for hostesses. The idea of getting paid for allowing lonely toffs to buy me bottles of champagne was by no means bereft of appeal, and the next thing I knew I was off to be seen by the hostess recruitment manager of a well-known private gentlemen's club just off Piccadilly. He got an earful of my elegant accent and an eyeful of my famous long legs, fondled his cigar suggestively, picked shreds of tobacco off his tongue, leered, leered some more, and asked when I could start. I could start immediately.

Hold on there, girlfriend. First I had to receive my orientation from the hostess 'mother', a masculine woman called Janet who, in an earlier decade, could probably have made her living playing a despoiler of naive virgins in homophobic B movies. Once having captured the fancy of a lonely gentleman in the upstairs bar area, I was to whisk him downstairs and get him to order as much ludicrously overpriced food and especially drink as possible. As far as the food was concerned, I was to order as though I'd been fasting for the preceding two weeks. Regarding the champagne, I was to make as much of it disappear as quickly as possible without actually drinking it. In the early going, I should watch carefully to see how the other girls disposed of it when their momentary boyfriends happened to glance elsewhere. For instance, I was to observe that the girls commonly forgot to put their glasses of champagne down before excusing themselves to leave for the loo, the better to empty them down the sink once they got there. It was crucial that I not allow myself to be observed leaving with one of our patrons at evening's end, as the police were absolutely itching to do us for prostitution. If I wanted to meet a patron off the premises in my free time, that was strictly my own business.

I wasn't mad about the wink she gave me during that last bit, but I had a job to do, and bought myself a white basque, white stockings, and white high-heeled sandals to do it in. Thus attired, I felt cold and vulnerable and not a little silly on the first night as I seated myself at the bar, crossed my famous legs, and ordered something with which to douse my inhibitions. If I continued to languish there, I remembered, I would earn nothing.

My fellow hostesses were lined up by the door, foxes at the gala opening of a new henhouse, waiting to pounce on whomever ventured through it. 'Do let's go home,' a familiar little voice inside whispered to me, more and more insistently as time went by. 'We're a nice girl, and don't belong among these rapacious tarts.'

An hour passed, and another. I hadn't earned a farthing, whatever a farthing was. It would cost me £10 to get a taxi home. I had to do what I had to do.

A gentleman came through the door. I grabbed him. Another hostess did likewise. I pulled him this way, and she that. She bared her teeth. Bare away, bitch, I thought – this one's mine.

He looked at me. He looked at her. He looked once more at both of us. He *was* mine. We went to the bar and I made him feel fascinating. He was a deep-sea diver, and not unpresentable. Working for oil companies, he earned more money than he knew what to do with. He wanted to spend some of it on a night with me. 'How much would it take to get you to say yes?' he asked. '£300?'

My head reeled. I barely cleared £800 pounds in a month working for ITV. And I nonetheless heard myself informing him that I couldn't accept money for sex.

His eyebrows climbed higher on his forehead. His blue eyes twinkled mischievously. '£400?' he wondered.

As though in a bad film, I heard the voices of the fine folks at my bank reverberating maddeningly. 'I can't,' I repeated.

His eyebrows went even higher. Far below them, his eyes did more twinkling. And then, with a shrug, he was gone, making the day of one of my esteemed colleagues.

Now a different inner voice was heard. 'Oh, nice one, Mansfield. You and the undiscovered alcoholic genius you adore can barely manage the price of a toilet roll, and here you are sending this perfectly nice deep-sea diver into the clutches of some slut from whom he's sure to catch something.'

'You're right,' I acknowledged sadly, alarming the barman, who quickly provided another glassful of attenuated principles.

A rotund red-faced man waddled woozily over, reeking of his beverage of choice. Panicking, I thought to try to snatch the deep-sea diver out of the clutches of the slut to whom he'd resigned himself, but he was nowhere to be seen now. 'Buy you a drink?' Ronnie Redface slobbered. I pictured poor Vladimir trying to roll himself a joint from seeds and stems. I pictured our depleted larder. Once more the bank manager's voice reverberated in my inner ear. 'Oh, would you?' I replied, batting my eyelashes, hating myself as I never had before.

The poor devil had already had a snootful. In trying to remove a single £20 note from his fat wallet, he managed to make a dozen more flutter to the floor. He giggled and knelt to pick them up, and then tried to stuff them down the front of my basque, but couldn't manage it. We hostesses were expressly forbidden to accept money while in the bar. Sod it, I thought, and stuffed the lot into my purse. How gloriously dignified I felt.

And it got worse. Determined not to be the only girl who hadn't managed to lure a victim downstairs, I batted my eyelashes again and asked if he fancied some dinner and dancing. He fancied them a treat, in fact, and I managed to get him downstairs in one piece. The requisite bottle of inferior, but outrageously overpriced, sparkling wine appeared as though by magic on our table. He poured, getting more on the table than in our glasses. I groped for small talk and asked what work he did. 'MP,' he slobbered.

Now he picked up the conversational ball. 'What,' he drooled lasciviously, 'would you think of the idea of selling me your knickers?' I shuddered visibly with revulsion, but he was too near to passing out to notice. 'Can't,' I finally managed. 'Need 'em.'

I got home and counted up how much I'd 'earned' – £120. In an evening.

It wasn't nearly enough, though, to compensate for the nausea I was experiencing just thinking of what I'd done, or the self-loathing. I bathed at great length and finally emerged from the tub feeling filthy and disgusting. I didn't even get into bed for fear that the stench that was surely coming off me would wake Vladimir. I stayed up all night and phoned the well-known private gentlemen's club the first moment I knew someone would be there to answer, to tell them I quit.

Out of the frying pan and into the fire, or, to be more accurate, the pizza oven. A restaurant called Pizza Hut (heretofore unknown on these shores) was going to open in Oxford Street, and needed waitresses. It occurred to me that I'd probably have made more selling my knickers to Ronnie Redface than I would in a week of delivering pizzas to hungry diners, but delivering pizzas to hungry diners wasn't going to make me want to scrub myself so hard that my epidermis nearly came off, so I applied. And got hired. And got trained.

Opening night came. The manager, who unmistakably had his eye on me, convened the staff and told us that we were to accept no payment – opening night was on the house!

There were no mobile phones in those days, but there was a pay phone downstairs, right between the Gents and Ladies. It was remarkable how urgently everyone seemed to need the toilet all of a sudden. I managed to elbow my way to the phone and to alert Vladimir to the fact that he could come and eat free before I, in turn, got elbowed aside by another waitress with the same idea, albeit a different boyfriend.

I was hardly more cut out for waitressing than I'd been for

hostessing. The rudeness of people! The condescension! The voices reverberating in my mind's ear now were those of my own mum and dad. A customer would say, 'Bring me a medium pepperoni,' and Mum and Dad would, as one, append, 'Please!' I managed to keep my mouth shut and the pizzas coming.

I very much enjoyed telling people at the end that their meals were free. So this, I thought, revelling in the joy that swept over their faces, is how Bowie feels when he looks at the first few rows. Then the most remarkable thing happened. A guy became irate when I told him his meal had been the Hut's treat. 'What are you on about?' he demanded, his face all darkness and distrust.

'We're [the corporate we!] just trying to build up good will among the pizza lovers of London,' I said, sure he'd change his tune completely when he understood the situation.

'That's the daftest thing I've ever heard,' he growled. 'How are you going to stay in business giving your bloody pizza away?' He wasn't drunk, I didn't think. His speech wasn't at all slurred, and I hadn't served him a drop.

I managed to keep smiling. 'It's just for tonight, you see. It won't be an ongoing policy.'

He shook his head disgustedly and put six quid on the table. 'Well, I don't accept handouts,' he said, getting up. 'Not from bloody Pizza Hut, and not from anybody else either.'

I managed to get the attention of our impossibly harried manager long enough to find out that I could keep the money. Vladimir arrived, literally smacking his lips, rubbing his gifted hands together in anticipation, accompanied by all of his band

and the girlfriends of a couple of his bandmates. He knew enough not to get seated in my section.

A party of two was led to the table that Mr No Handouts had just vacated. The female half was around forty-five and extremely common, wearing too much perfume, huge hoop earrings, and a miniskirt that she shouldn't have, as her legs weren't nearly up to the job. The male half was in his early fifties, with a ruddy complexion and eyebrows so faint he seemed not to have any.

When I brought their pizza, the female was in the loo or something. The guy made no bones about his interest in me. We were required by order of Her Majesty the Queen, or at least Pizza Hut corporate policy, to ask, as we delivered a pizza, if there were anything else the customer would like. I asked.

'Now that you mention it, darling,' the guy said, making no greater effort to conceal his leering than Ronnie Redface had back at the gentlemen's club, 'I'd quite like a bit of crumpet.' We hadn't discussed it specifically in the course of training, but I suspected that Pizza Hut corporate policy frowned on slapping customers' faces. So I just smiled wanly.

'You really are the ticket,' he said. 'You know that?'

I smiled even more wanly. No luck. 'I'm a leg man,' he said, his eyes descending below my waist and staying there. I wondered if they had wandered below the waist of the woman in the big hoop earrings. 'And you have a really gorgeous pair.'

His charming girlfriend returned, bless her heart. 'What's all this then?' she demanded in an accent as common as her attire.

He turned to her and shrugged. 'I think they're encouraged

to be flirtatious.' He turned back to me and said I could run along now. He did not get his pint of lager spilled over his head, and lo, it was a miracle.

The next night, everyone had to pay for the pizzas, but that didn't make those who sat in my section less rude or condescending. After three months of working at ITV from 9 to 5.30 p.m., and three nights a week between 6 p.m. and 1 a.m. at Pizza Hut, there was hardly enough left of me to sprinkle on pasta.

My sacrifice had served only to drive a wedge between me and Vladimir, who'd come to feel neglected during my long absences. I consoled myself by allowing Pizza Hut's manager – who apparently was a leg man himself, and who was pally with a catering company that fed itinerant rock stars and their entourages – to sneak me into the Hammersmith Odeon and Milton Keynes venues of Mr Bowie's *Serious Moonlight* tour.

And I do mean sneak. Waiving the decorousness that would later come to characterise my style as the supreme dominant goddess of all London, I entered the Milton Keynes show under blankets in one of the catering trucks, canapés to the left of me, crudités to the right. Later, rather more glamorously, I had an opportunity to snort cocaine on Himself's actual tour bus, and leapt at it.

Getting home sniffing from that glorious mad weekend, I discovered that Vladimir, crazed with jealousy, oblivious to the number of pizzas I'd served for his art, had moved out of our Belsize Park flat.

Which, despite all the painful bits, meant much shorter hours for me.

CHAPTER FIVE

Doing it with a Girlie

I soon vacated the flat myself, put it up for sale, and moved in with Doubtless's keyboard player's girlfriend Julie in picturesque Clapham, only to be reminded of the ancient knowledge that great buddies often make rotten flatmates. I fled – platonically! – into the arms of a new friend called Hermione, who knew everyone who was anyone in London rock circles, including David Bowie's ex-wife Angie, as well as a great many who were no one at all. At once a cunning minx and mercenary airhead, Hermione, the daughter of a slattern who spent her every evening at casinos picking up men, yearned only to marry a rock star, towards which end she had long legs, red hair, and a closetful of slutty attire. Hoping to snag some of her runoff, I moved in with her.

She began immediately to set me up on dates with men she wasn't interested in. One of them, Joe, was very pretty, tall and skinny, and drove a Datsun 240Z in which I soon became a regular passenger. He was bright, witty, blond, and gorgeous, wore the tightest trousers in London, had the biggest cock I'd ever seen, and could fuck for days at a time – all of which served to make up for his never allowing me on top, his unnervingly close relationship with his shotgun, and his alarming penchant for hurrying from our bed every morning as the sun rose. About a month into our romance, I realised I'd never glimpsed him in daylight, decided that he was one of the undead, and did what any sensible girl would have done in like circumstances – rented a flat with him in Finchley Central, from a mad Irish nurse landlady who ensured that we were never without vodka.

No amount of booze, though, could obscure that he was pathologically jealous, and that what was good for the goose didn't apply to the gander. While he insisted, whenever I went out, on picking me up, he regularly disappeared for days at a time. He knew a great many prostitutes, and would often decide on the spur of the moment to visit them – To Drop Something Off – while I squirmed in the passenger seat of the 240Z, wondering at great length what that something might be. I never saw him on Sundays, and was pretty sure that he wasn't spending the day in church. His absences grew ever more extended. He always had a credible explanation, but a little voice inside my head said, 'You prat, you.'

When I got home late from a drink with a friend one evening, he pulled me out of the cab by my hair, demanding at the top of his lungs to know where, and with whom, I'd been, and dousing me with the orange juice he'd been drinking. I managed to wrest free, and spent a sleepless night upstairs in the mad Irish nurse's flat, crying. I went to the police the following morning, the hair Joe hadn't pulled out matted with dried orange juice, to report that he'd threatened my life. The desk sergeant yawned and said that they were powerless to do anything until he'd actually hurt me.

For the next ten days, my life was a nightmare, as he refused to relinquish his keys, and the mad Irish nurse somehow never managed to have our lock changed. Joe would let himself in, we'd bellow at one another, and I'd flee. Returning on one occasion, I found that he'd shredded my wardrobe and shoes, piled them in the middle of the lounge, and destroyed the photos I'd hung on the walls.

When finally I got my own locksmith, Joe took to parking right outside the flat and revving the 240Z's engine menacingly, and hung a dead bird outside the window.

But it got worse. One night Lizzie, the Ritz croupier sister of one of Joe's best friends, turned up very distraught looking for him. As gently as possible, I enquired what she wanted him for. 'Well, he's my bloody boyfriend, isn't he?' she blurted, bursting into sobs.

She had Sundays off.

The rotter had been seeing both of us for months!

And Lizzie believed herself pregnant.

We sobbed in one another's arms.

As though in a bad sitcom, the three of us repaired to a nearby pub to try to make sense of the situation, but it defied us. I told Joe – henceforth and forevermore Joe the Woe – that

I hoped never to see him again, as too did Lizzie. It took me years to become able to endure the mere sight of him. And a few more years for him to offer to take me, to compensate me for the destruction of my wardrobe and shoes and photographs, to Poland to see the only bison herd in all Europe.

I'm not making this up. I still have the unspeakably hideous bison-head clock, which hasn't told the time since five minutes after I got it back to London, on the wall of my kitchen to prove it.

I decided it wasn't enough to be besotted by pop stars who were or at least pretended quite convincingly to be gay. Nothing would do for me but to experience homosexuality for myself. Having got wind of a club in Brixton called the Fridge that had Lesbian Nites on Wednesdays, I got tarted up a treat. 'Just what precisely do you imagine you're *doing*?' the Mouse, so long unheard from – and so little missed – demanded. I took off all my makeup and attractive clothing, watched *Tomorrow's World* for ten minutes, felt ashamed of myself for being such a little wuss, put everything back on, and hurried to the tube station before the Mouse's adult education class ended and she got back on line.

Two hours later, I found myself feeling a perfect gooseberry in the half-empty club, surrounded by women in couples. I gathered up my handbag, which I'd brought instead of a big sign reading *I Don't Belong*, even though the effect would have been identical (real men don't eat quiche, and real dykes don't carry bags). Standing up, I found my way blocked by a small, rather hefty woman with spiky jet black hair, wonderfully excessive eye makeup, and leather trousers. 'Do you come here often?' she asked, or something along those lines. We told one another our names – hers was Linda – and were joined by her tall, lanky butch friend, Julie, who was rather less appealing to me in her Homosexual International Conspiracy-sanctioned uniform of shapeless T-shirt, jeans, and crewcut.

I can get on a treat with nearly anyone except my sister Fiona, and got on a treat with them. At evening's end, Linda asked where I lived. When I told her, she insisted that, rather than taking a taxi ride that a great many developing nations wouldn't have been able to afford, I spend the night at their place. 'Why not?' I agreed, slurring a little.

By the time we were back at their lovenest, we were all thirsty again. Linda broke open some Jack Daniels. Julie, peepers all a-droop, declared herself too pooped to pop, and disappeared into the bedroom. Within a couple of heartbeats Linda was kneeling between my legs telling me how attractive she found me and how much she'd enjoy kissing me. A moment later, that's exactly what she was doing, but the lusty snoring in the next room and my distaste for Linda's girth conspired to keep our knickers on.

I may not have wanted to know her carnally, but I liked her well enough to accompany her to most of the capital's gay clubs, including the notorious (by virtue of having been depicted in *The Killing of Sister George*) Gateways, just off the King's Road in Chelsea. The testosterone level was very much higher there than in the clubs I was accustomed to, the women bigger, more muscular, and with thicker facial hair than my eyelinered boyfriends. I realised that she took me there to show me off as her latest conquest – never mind that I remained to be conquered. While Linda went to get drinks, I cowered piteously in a corner while mobs of bulging-biceped women, far more unashamedly predatory than any man I'd ever encountered, sauntered over to determine if I fancied a game of hide-the-ferret. I didn't ask. I thought I was happier not knowing.

Linda became one of my best friends, taking me to clubs, buying me dinner, showering me with gifts, but never getting in my pants. Eventually she got fed up and married the owner – a man, mind you – of a travel company in Amsterdam. 'Graham's my soulmate,' Linda explained, a little sheepishly. 'I can't help that he's male, can I?' I disliked him from the first moment we met.

They invited me to the Netherlands for the weekend. After a very long night, they pissed off to their bedroom, and I to the sofa bed, wherein I was enjoying the deep slumber of the innocent and very drunk when I realised I had company, that someone – the noxious Graham! – was playing with (a) my hair and (b) himself. I shot out of bed as though on fire, demanding to know what he thought he was doing. 'I thought,' he explained, very memorably, if not at all credibly, 'that you might fancy some company.'

I did indeed, but that of another guitarist, though in this new one's case, 'guitarist' was a liberal definition of the term. He had bleached blond hair, wore makeup and frilly shirts, and called himself Koinneach, even though his family and childhood friends knew him as Tommy. I think he'd chosen Koinneach as a gesture of solidarity with the memory of James Joyce, or because he perversely fancied the idea of no one outside a few academics in Dublin being able to spell his name properly. After the alcoholic, substance-abusing Vladimir and the volatile Joe, he was a breath of fresh air. He didn't drink, he had a job, and he drove – albeit some very old classic motorcycles, rather than lovely spacious coupés that would have been very much gentler on my coiffures. I first glimpsed him at Gossips – one look at his tight leather trousers, bleached hair, and eyeliner and I shuddered with lust. I shuddered even more on learning that he was a member of a glam band the Japanese had clasped to their collective breast in a big way. Never mind that he played the guitar only slightly better than I did, and I didn't play at all.

Once having got wind of my interest, Koinneach wooed me both frenziedly and with great panache. He sent me flowers at work. He wrote me little love letters in the shade of lipstick he'd been wearing the night our eyes first met. He'd be standing outside ITV House when I got off work, with a box of chocolates in hand – provided a mob of local labourers hadn't relieved him of them. He absolutely showered me with compliments. My lips! My eyes! My calves! My thighs! My knees! My ankles! My toes! My towering intellect! There were too few hours in the day for him to praise any of them adequately, but he tried – oh, did he! He opened doors for me, and pulled out my chair in romantic bistros.

When he revealed that he shared my attraction to pretty young boys, I confessed that I quite fancied the idea of making love to another woman, and we proceeded to have huge fun in the clubs ogling both sexes. My twenty-third birthday approached.

And then arrived. He rang to ask me to be at his place in Bow at seven. I said I'd been thinking in terms of a candlelit dinner at a romantic bistro first. He sounded a bit exasperated. 'I've got something for you that I can't give you in a romantic bistro,' he explained, clearly wishing he hadn't had to.

I arrived a few minutes before seven. He offered me a glass of Chardonnay and glanced repeatedly at his watch. He paced. I sipped. He paced. I implored him to sit down, as he was making me nervous. He obliged. He looked at his wristwatch. I sipped and wondered. It was 7:05, and then 7:07, and then 7:10.

The bell sounded. He leapt from his chair as though electrically shocked. He swung open the door and Jamie Lee Curtis sauntered in, or at least a tall, boyish, ever-so-cute young woman who, in the same circumstances that Vladimir might have evoked Keith Richards, vividly evoked the famous film star. 'Meet Daphne,' Koinneach urged me, beside himself with delight now. 'She's your birthday present.'

We all grinned at one another like idiots. Not at all unappetising, our Daphne.

'I've told Daphne about how you quite fancy the idea of doing it with a girlie,' Koinneach informed me, embarrassing me frightfully. And then it was poor Daphne's turn. 'After I described you,' he said, 'Daphne quite fancied the idea of being the girlie you did it with.'

A bit more idiotic grinning, and then this compliant vision of cuteness and I were racing into the bedroom and having at one another with great, great enthusiasm at considerable, considerable length. All that I'd hoped for! Fun galore! Sign me up for the Bisexual Club! We fell asleep in one another's smooth white arms. What a birthday!

But then, a couple of hours hence, I woke up alone.

I rubbed the sleep from my little eyes and padded quietly into the lounge, to find there, on the floor, my boyfriend and new girlfriend very convincingly impersonating confirmed heterosexuals.

It was my birthday, and I would cry if I wanted to, and I did indeed want to, but not as much as I wanted the two of them to come back to bed with me. In view of the occasion, how could they decline?

We became quite the modern couple, Koinneach and I. Nights that we didn't spend in one another's loving embrace, we spent chasing pretty young men around, in his case, or, in mine, being seen in all the most fashionable gay and lesbian night spots with winsome Jamie Lee Curtis lookalikes. At one club's crossdressing night, Daphne and I, in cap and fedora and braces and trousers and rather less makeup than usual (mere ounces in my case, and not gallons) were photographed between tall men dressed as Little Bo Peep. Walking through Turnmills, we both had our arses pinched so prolifically that we had to stand on the train home.

You want to know about our lovemaking. You want to know which of us took the masculine role, and which the soft submissive. I must disappoint you, though, and reveal in all honesty that Daphne and I made love like two women, and not like a woman and a male surrogate, in the sense that we were both equally aggressive and docile. Rather than one ravaging the other, we conducted lots of tender explorations of one another's bodies. It was very sweet and very pleasant, but as we celebrated three months together, I realised that I wasn't really much of a bisexual. I found myself more and more longing for that part

of Koinneach that had originally made him Tommy, rather than
Sharon, say, or Margaret. Call me old-fashioned, but I came to
realise that nothing really compared for me – readers of delicate
sensibilities are warned to skip directly to the beginning of the
following paragraph – to having an enormous swollen cock very
deep inside.

We met for dinner on a September evening at a café near
Leicester Square. It was warm enough to dine *alfresco*. Daphne
fretted that I was being distant. She was a sweet person and I
was in no great hurry to injure her. I squeezed her hand under
the table and assured her that I didn't mean to seem that way.
I was aware of their ambiguity even as the words left my lips.
Just before our starter plates were taken away, a young rock god
in the tightest trousers in all London swaggered past with a mate.
He very much had the bum for the trousers. 'I don't know what
he looks like coming,' I sighed when I noted Daphne giving me
a sort of accusatory look, 'but I do very much enjoy watching
him go.'

'I was right in the middle of saying something to you,
Claire,' she pointed out, wounded, and began to cry. I told her
I was terribly sorry. She asked if I realised that ever since we'd
sat down together, I'd seemed to be a great deal more interested
in men walking past than in what she had to say. I began to
deny it, but my voice sounded hollow, even inside my own
head, where it had the benefit of reverberation. I acknowledged
that she was probably right, and told her again that I was very
sorry. She seemed to recognise that I wasn't speaking in just an
immediate sense. She stood up, put a £10 note on the table, and
said, 'I expect it's going to be a long while before I don't miss

you any more.' Then she turned on her heel, and walked out of my life.

My dad's new boss, the manager of the Tesco that had essentially put him out of business, was coming for dinner. Mum insisted that I stay to meet him. My dad would be proud to introduce me to Roger.

Dad was finding working at Tesco far less demoralising than he'd expected, and in fact was enjoying himself. He liked the lack of pressure. If he turned out to have ordered too much of a particular thing on a particular day, it wasn't nearly so worrisome as it had been at his own shop, where such a miscalculation was apt to have wiped out a day's profits. All he missed really was the one-to-one interaction with his favourite customers – and even some of them had begun to drift into Tesco. 'It was quite funny the first time I ran into Mrs Hobson there,' he chuckled. 'She looked guilty as sin, but when I pointed out my badge and told her that I was now First Assistant Manager, she felt a lot better. "As much as I enjoyed getting my fruit and veg from you all those years," she said, "there's just no beating Tesco's prices, is there?"'

Imagining how it might have made my dad feel, I'd have hated it if Roger were young enough to be his son, and so was pleased to see that he was in his early fifties, perhaps ten years younger than my dad. His breath suggested that he'd refreshed himself generously at the pub before turning up, but he wasn't merry, and he'd brought my mum a bouquet. I had the feeling I'd seen him somewhere before. My dad had said he was a confirmed bachelor, which I'd come to understand was code for gay, but he didn't seem it. After he'd demanded to know why my dad hadn't mentioned that he was married to one of the five most beautiful women in Ealing – pleasing my mum even more than the bouquet did – he aimed his charm gun at me and Fiona, telling my dad that we'd certainly got our mum's good looks, and that he hoped my dad was keeping an eye on us, lest we break so many hearts that the borough's morale take a precipitous drop. Actually, I'd always believed – in spite of the fact that she's my sister and I'm obligated to love her and I do, deep down, in spite of everything – that Fiona must be one of the five least attractive women in Greater London. Washing your hair once a month and wearing the same tracksuit and trainers every day and no trace of makeup will do that to a woman.

Roger, whom I was coming to feel more and more strongly I'd seen somewhere before, was absolutely incredulous at my mum's skill in the kitchen, and kept his palate fresh by dousing it after nearly every mouthful with a generous swig of Merlot. He'd embarrassed everyone else at the table, and now it was my dad's turn. As he, Roger, saw it, his recruitment of my dad was going to be one of the brightest stars on his own performance evaluation for the year. 'There's absolutely no substitute for experience,' he said, as though at a company breakfast, putting his fork down and a hand on my mortified *pater*'s shoulder, 'and in Harry Mansfield, I was able to bring nearly a quarter-century of it to Tesco.' He raised his glass. 'To Harry, and to Tesco, and to you, his beautiful family.' I thought Fiona might make herself be sick on his shoes, but she restrained herself.

'Well, it isn't as though Tesco left me a world of choice, of course,' my dad, not one of the great sentimentalists, pointed out. Roger just absolutely screamed with laughter, making it official that he was now pissed. He put his big pink hand on my dad's shoulder again and wheezed with laughter: 'No, I don't reckon that we did, did we? But that's your modern world for you, innit?'

The meal progressed. Mum served apple pie and custard for dessert. It was by far the most delicious apple pie and custard Roger had ever tasted. You couldn't help but envy the guy his great enthusiasm for absolutely everything. He thought a sip or two of brandy might be exactly what he needed as a coda to such a splendid meal. I could tell from the look on Mum's face that she'd have much preferred his waiting to be offered.

It turned out that he was very keen on classical music, his favourites being Brahms and Chopin. He'd brought cigars for him and Dad to enjoy with their brandy, but Mum didn't allow smoking in her house. 'The shape of things to come,' he sighed. 'Give 'em a year or two, and the second-hand smoke fascists'll be as powerful as they are in America. Do you know, Harry, that when I was in Philadelphia last year, you couldn't smoke in a bloody cinema? Everybody on the screen's having a fag, and you're sitting there coming out of your skin craving one. Ah, well. At least we'll all live for ever now there's so many places you can't indulge.'

'I just can't bear the smell,' Mum said, actually managing to sound apologetic, 'how it lingers in the curtains like it does. If it's terribly important, you can go out in the back garden.'

Roger looked to my dad to see if he'd have any company. 'I've never smoked,' Dad said, shrugging. 'Never had any interest really.'

Roger looked fairly miserable, but brightened when Mum asked if he needed a bit more brandy. By now, I was absolutely twitching, trying to remember where I'd seen him before. I headed upstairs to the loo, to which I had a satisfying visit.

Roger was waiting outside when I opened the door. He didn't get out of my way, but gave me an admiring head-to-toes-to-head. It was summer, and sweltering, and I was wearing shorts. 'Has anybody ever told you,' he asked, 'that you have a really gorgeous set of gams?'

Oh, marvellous. Not just someone old enough to be my dad, but my dad's boss coming on to me. I tried to signal to him how inappropriate I found his compliment by not thanking him for it, but only smiling wanly. It didn't budge him. 'If you ever fancy having a curry or something together, or even a drink, get Harry to let me know.'

Oh, absolutely. I'm sure Dad wouldn't feel even a little awkward about that. Jesus.

I gave him another small smile, wanner than the first, and looked longingly past him down the stairs. He continued to stand his ground. 'You might be thinking that I'm a hell of a lot older than you,' he said, giving me a faceful of his not entirely fragrant breath. 'Well, all I can say is that the gun still shoots, if you know what I mean.'

That didn't deserve even a wan smile, and I wasn't going to stick around to find out what came next. I pushed past him and went back downstairs, at first intent on relating our little interaction, but then realising, two seconds later, that nothing good would come of my doing so.

And then I remembered where I'd seen him and his faint

eyebrows before – Pizza Hut in Oxford Street, the night it opened, with the common thick-legged woman in the miniskirt and huge hoop earrings.

He pushed his luck, giving me a wink when he came back downstairs. I still saw no good coming of my blowing the whistle on him, and left to go home without having said a word.

A short time later, I got together with Fiona for a drink. It was hard for me to hear about her painful loneliness without trying to help her figure out ways to rescue herself from it. I often urged her to take a bit more pride in her appearance, and did so over this drink. To which she, neck-deep in denial, sniffed, 'Well, I was attractive enough for that Tesco bloke Mum and Dad had over a few weeks back, wasn't I?'

Roger had tried to pull her as well.

CHAPTER SIX

Dry Heaving to Mecca

I'd been only a short while at ITV when they launched their vaunted and long-awaited second commercial channel. Channel 4 was to be all that ITV hadn't been to that point – adventurous, occasionally controversial, generally geared to a viewer with an IQ higher than room temperature. On the afternoon of the launch, jackbooted thugs escorted us employees from our desks to the viewing theatre to witness en masse the birth of the new baby. We clapped and cheered dutifully as the new channel's logo and jingle appeared, and transmission began.

I had always thought of myself as an animal lover, and couldn't abide cruelty of any sort. One of my earliest memories is of being inconsolable on learning that worms have no eyes. To that point, though, I had only just dipped my toe into animal activism, to the tune of attending several rallies in Trafalgar Square and protesting outside the Canadian Embassy against the annual massacre of Newfoundland baby harp seals. Oblivious to my personal culpability, I would then enjoy a pepperoni pizza.

That evening when I got home to my Belsize Park shoebox, I told Vladimir that I planned to watch Channel 4's broadcast of *The Animals Film*, an apparently very unsettling documentary of animal abuse worldwide, from factory farming to vivisection, from circuses and fur production to hunting. 'Sod that,' he replied thirstily, and repaired to the local hostelry, leaving me to witness on my own the unspeakable horror that the film depicted unflinchingly. I was transfixed from the very first scene, in which a gentle captive-born elephant trustingly follows his keeper to a set of four ankle shackles, and waits patiently while the shackles are fitted and electrodes laced over his body. Moments later, as a massive current is passed through him, his trunk stiffens, his eyes pop, his sides convulse, and, after a seeming eternity of suffering, he finally collapses to the ground. 'An early experiment with electricity' the caption tersely informs us.

I was deeply shocked, nauseated, in tears, but there was much more to follow – image after image of unspeakable barbarity, accompanied by no editorial comment whatever, the idea being that it was down to the viewer to come to his own conclusions. As the film continued, rage crept in to keep my horror company. When finally it was over, I turned off the TV and sat alone in the darkness, utterly numb. Vladimir staggered home from the pub to find me mute.

The next morning, I opened the fridge to find the packet of bacon I'd bought only the day before – and realised that I held in my hands part of the pathetic remains of what had once been a creature with a personality, intelligence, and integrity – a creature that had been abused from the moment of its birth and ultimately been brutally murdered so that other animals could savour the taste of its flesh. I'd become vegetarian.

Oh, what an insufferable dining companion I was for a while, with my endless disapproving references to the 'dead things' on the plates of others, but it wasn't until John Latimer-Davies noticed my anti-fur T-shirt one afternoon atop the 134 in Muswell Hill that I went really gung-ho. Grizzled, bewhiskered, very near burnout, John hadn't much fight left in him, but I was breathing fire, and no longer remotely content with sending £10 off to this or that charity. Slavery had once been lawful, and the disenfranchisement of women. Unjust laws cried out to be defied, and I was itching to defy them.

John gave me contact information for a group in Greater London that regularly protested against animal abuse, and before you could say, 'Do you have any conception of how utterly wretched was the life of the animal whose flesh you're about to eat?' I was among the most implacable animal rights activists in the capital. Every Sunday morning I was one of the most vocal protestors in front of the Leyden Street poultry slaughterhouse in Petticoat Lane Market, where, in accordance with *halal* tradition, fully conscious birds had their throats slit. Not even the unspeakable stench of the place – a stench so appalling that even the police, whose thankless job it was to keep us from storming the building, held their noses –

could deter me, not with ducks and battery hens screaming within.

After one of my fellow protestors, noting my boots, gently
pointed out that leather was just fur with the hair scraped off, I
renounced it for ever. Years later, when I became the supreme
dominant goddess of all London, I would stick staunchly to my
guns, wearing only PVC and other manmade fibres.

I became the PR officer for the Shark Protection League,
which annually protested the UK's biggest shark angling festival, in Looe, Cornwall. The League had been down the two years
previous to my joining, and got a lot of media attention, but the
struggle was far from over – and was getting nasty. Seeing us
in town in our Shark Protection League sweatshirts, some of the
locals demanded to know where we were staying, and we got the
impression it wasn't so they could bring us homemade pasties.

In fact, pretending to be a group of young Christians on an
adventure holiday, we'd booked into a farmhouse miles from
Looe, which meant that we had to rise at half-four every morning
to arrive in time to confront the anglers before they went out to
sea. The local press found this jolly good stuff – very much
livelier than their usual enquiries into whether Farmer Giles's
prize-winning marrow had been a fix. I gave everyone who asked
a lively interview, mentioning, for instance, the fact that sharks
commonly coughed up their entire stomachs trying to escape the
anglers' hooks. After running the gauntlet of gurning villagers,
we'd hurry back to the farmhouse to watch the interviews on
TV. Then in the late afternoon it was back to Looe to confront
the heroic anglers once more.

The festival ended. We protestors went home. I'd been back

in London for barely a day when I learned that its organisers had decided to call off the following year's festival. Due to lack of interest.

Would you be able to forgive me if I said that my elation was short-lived because I had much bigger fish to fry?

For years, various environmental and animal rights groups around the UK had regarded Moskowitz Shoes, the UK's most prolific manufacturer of reptile-skin footwear, as the embodiment of corporate nefariousness. I joined in regular demonstrations outside the company's headquarters in Bow, just down the road from Koinneach's digs, proudly brandishing a placard I'd made myself, which was intended to inform onlookers of the vast numbers of animals sacrificed to make the tasselled loafers on which Moskowitz spent nearly £1 billion annually in advertising to make stockbrokers believe the shoes were essential footwear for work.

The handy thing about having Moskowitz as an adversary was that, no matter where you happened to be, one of their ghastly boutiques was always nearby. We protestors would collect boxes bearing the corporation's logo and then deposit what we'd collected in huge sacks outside the front doors of their head office, which we'd then sit down in front of, making it difficult for their staff to get in. Ultimately, the police would be summoned to drag us away.

At night I'd turn on the news and see Derek Whatsit, as I'll call Moskowitz's preternaturally charming spokesman, seeming to exude both compassion for those of us manhandled by the Old Bill and great sadness about our belief that Moskowitz's

was breeding alligators just to murder them for their hides.
Nothing could have been more obvious than that Truth and
Justice were of absolutely paramount importance to this guy. He
was the man every woman wanted and every man wanted to be
– handsome but not pretty, sensitive but not effete, terribly clever
but absolutely down-to-earth. And I knew that all across Britain,
people were turning to their partners and saying, 'You know, I
quite trust that bloke. What he's saying must be true.' And it
drove me and everyone else in the animal rights movement half
mad with frustration.

I had given ITV my all. Well, my most. Well, rather a lot.
And still I waited to be promoted. And waited and waited.
And waited. It had been eight bloody years, for Christ's sake.
It wasn't that management thought me a twat – far from it,
in fact. I had been told repeatedly that I would surely ascend
the corporate ladder with dizzying alacrity if only I would not
do things like impersonate Boy George – and with considerable
panache! – at the office Christmas party. I resolved to – forgive
me – go for it. Not even being required, after a departmental
shuffle, to report to the most insufferable arsehole in the United
Kingdom could weaken my resolve.

He called himself Georges, although there was only one
of him, and was an ardent francophile, to the tune of smoking
300 Gauloise cigarettes per day, bathing insufficiently frequently, reeking of garlic even on those infrequent occasions
when he had bathed, and glowering at me homicidally when
I spoke English in his presence. We loathed one another on
sight.

A Copy Executive – in charge of ensuring that the TV and radio commercials we broadcast didn't lie too outrageously – position opened up about a year after Georges became my boss. Having already been doing the job for ages on a *de facto* basis, I applied for it formally, and submitted to two gruelling interviews, during which I exuded charm, confidence, and competence.

It was commonly understood in the office that I'd been shortlisted for the job, along with two others. I hadn't wanted anything so much since those tickets to see Mr Bowie at the Marquee. But wishing didn't make it so. They opted for a smart young thing without ten minutes' experience, but with a degree. I gave a week's notice. At once the department essentially ceased to function, as my colleagues, who agreed unanimously that I should have got the job, suddenly developed debilitating headaches.

I was taken out for a leaving drink. My colleagues showered me with gifts and platitudes of regret, and then, having had far too much to drink, hanged in Soho Square effigies of the group heads responsible for my fatal disgruntlement.

I quite enjoyed not working nine-to-five. I quite disliked not being able to afford my train fare to the West End. I did what I had to do: silver service waitressing for corporate clients for a posh caterer, selling kitchenware, managing a bargain bookshop in Muswell Hill, signing on as a retail assistant at the Muswell Hill Woolies during their Christmas rush, cleaning house and ironing for a family in East Finchley, delivering cards for a local cab firm, and, most importantly, managing an electrical store in Highgate owned by Arturo, a mate of Joe the Woe's.

Arturo notwithstanding, the staff were all British, and thus could hardly wait to dash across the road to the pub at day's end. 'Twas there that I came to know Fuller, the scruffy little bloke who spent his workday in our basement repairing hairdryers and toasters. It turned out that he fancied the same sort of loud guitar-based rock that I had come to like, and, having messed about with a friend's CB gear, dreamed of starting a pirate radio station. What fun, I thought, and set about learning as much as I could about broadcasting – which, given my extraordinarily high native intelligence, was quite a lot.

We set up a little transmitter on Hampstead Heath. No go. Trying to set up a rather larger one in Barnet, we were vilified by the wives of local farmers. But then we met a chap who was willing to build us one with a bit of welly, found ourselves a lovely tall tower block on which to set it up, and were away. We called ourselves Rock FM, our imagination having been expended on organising the transmitter.

I was like Mr Toad at the advent of the motorcar – hopelessly hooked, absolutely transformed. I could say whatever I chose about my favourite records, and countless dozens of persons I hadn't even met out there in Radioland would chuckle, or growl, or tap their toes in time, or otherwise be moved! We built up our on-air hours and recruited new presenters. Reviewers in *Time Out* and *City Limits* hailed us as gloriously hip, a wonderful change from ordinary radio. Better yet, Radio Caroline, which had been driving the UK authorities mad for three decades by illegally broadcasting to Europe from the North

Sea, invited us out for a tour of the Mecca of pirate radio, the *Ross Revenge*, the one-time Ross Frozen Foods fishing trawler from which they broadcast.

But how would we get out to it?

It turned out that one of our DJs, 'Squeaky' Mark Rogers, whose speaking voice, when he got excited, was audible only to dogs, owned a 30-foot yacht berthed in Harwich.

'Oh, no, you're not,' Mum and Dad said when I told them of my forthcoming adventure. 'Are you mad?' wondered my friends. The last time I'd been on a ferry, I'd been quite sensationally sick, and my strong aversion to physical exertion had precluded my learning to swim, but I could not be dissuaded.

The night before we were to visit the *Ross Revenge*, four of us boarded Squeaky's yacht, consumed much, much beer, and tittered appreciatively as our host pulled condoms over his head and inflated them from the inside. Then we received word that Caroline, moored only an hour from us two days before, had had to sail farther out to sea to elude the authorities. Damn the torpedoes, we all agreed, barely able to stand.

At five o'clock the next morning, the irrepressible Squeaky woke us with a full cooked English breakfast. Knowing that I would need my strength, I ate more than my share of fried eggs, tomatoes, beans, and toast, and we cast off. Hurrah! Next stop: adventure!

Actually, not. Next stop: severe nausea. Thirty minutes after we'd weighed anchor, I realised I'd turned green. Ten minutes after that, my breakfast came back up on me, and then disappeared over the side into the choppy grey waters. Ten minutes after that, I began fervently to wish that I were dead. And ten minutes after that, even though there was nothing left in my stomach, I took to dry-heaving every twenty minutes like clockwork, to the infinite amusement of Squeaky and Fuller. In only three more hours, we were in sight of the *Ross*, so what right did I have to grumble?

I could not have begun to describe my relief at seeing how huge – and presumably stable – the *Ross* was. Nor, by the same token, could I have begun to describe the dread that filled me on realising that, by virtue of its deck being thirty feet above our own, we had to wait for a swell to elevate us halfway up the *Ross*'s side, and then leap into one of the gigantic tyres lashed to it.

Yeah, right.

Oh, no, you're not. Are you mad? As though in a bad film, the voices of my loved ones reverberated in my mind's ear.

Here came a swell – a bloody gigantic bugger. Our little yacht lurched upwards. 'Do it!' screamed Fuller, and do it I did – I closed my eyes and leapt. And there I was, as our yacht fell away behind me, alone on a gigantic tyre on the side of a trawler in the middle of the North Sea. I thought I'd devote a moment or two to abject terror, but before I knew what was going on, rough hands – angel's hands! – were grabbing me at all points and dragging me unceremoniously over the side and on to the deck.

Bliss! I felt as though back on land. And this was Caroline, the selfsame Caroline I'd listened to through an earphone under my pillow when my parents thought me sound asleep. Nirvana!

I felt better almost immediately. We were shown the hold,

the transmitter mast, the galley, the staff's living quarters, and the actual studio. But what was that frightful racket? Oh, not to worry. It was only our little yacht being bashed to kindling against the side of the *Ross* by the fast-worsening weather. Which meant – oh, yes! – that after less than an hour's respite, we had to reboard our yacht instantly and sail back across the Atlantic, or whatever they called the ocean we'd had to cross to get out here.

Reboarding the yacht was very much like disembarking from it, except rather more terrifying. I was lowered over the side by my denim jacket and leopard print jeans, my little feet frantically trying to find the tyre, the merciless sea churning malevolently below, my destination crashing again and again and again against the *Ross*'s side. A swell came. I leapt without hesitation – could drowning be any worse than enduring the voyage back to Harwich? I landed on all fours, slid halfway across the deck, crawled weeping to where I had spent the earlier voyage, wedged myself into a corner, and apologised to the Goddess for every unkind word I'd ever said, every tiniest sin.

It didn't work.

It was at least six months and 7000 dry heaves before our skipper at last squeaked, 'Land ahoy!' – the most beautiful words in the English language. Fuller came and prised my frozen little hands off the ropes they'd been clutching for the entire voyage and pulled me to my feet.

I was so grateful to be back on land that I married the first man I saw, bore him three strapping sons, and lived the rest of my life as a humble fishwife. If anyone was entitled to a little hyperbole, it was I.

In fact, having been too terrified and nauseated to pee for the past six hours, I dashed as fast as my famous but now rubbery legs would take me into the Ladies of the nearest pub, and there beheld a sight of the most unspeakable horror – my own reflection. My long blonde hair was plastered to my face, rock hard from the salt of the merciless sea. Huge black blobs of mascara adorned my cheeks. Long streams of eye shadow were racing for my chin. No wonder the locals had hidden their young from me.

I joined my fellow survivors. I drank a pint. What extraordinarily good fun I'd had.

And how very little I came to have as Rock FM began its third year of broadcasting. Our builder and our engineer, without whom we'd have been inaudible, demanded shows of their own – and then, once having got them, played Dire Straits and Fleetwood Mac and Dire Straits and Fleetwood Mac and Dire Straits and Fleetwood Mac and Dire Straits and Fleetwood Mac and Dire Straits and Fleetwood Mac and Dire Straits and Fleetwood Mac and Dire Straits and Fleetwood Mac and Dire Straits and Fleetwood Mac and Dire Straits and Fleetwood Mac and Dire Straits and Fleetwood Mac and Dire Straits and Fleetwood Mac and Dire Straits until I wanted to dry heave. The reviewers began to mock us, the listeners to turn elsewhere. I confronted Fuller. He was no happier about our benefactors' choice of music than I, but if we offended them, there went our perfect signal and virtually free transmitters.

I quit, and was almost immediately headhunted by Raiders FM, another pirate station that wanted me as their rock presenter.

The station's manager, Mick, had a troubling habit of staring soulfully into the eyes of impressionable young women he hoped to pull and huskily murmuring, 'You know, I'll bet you'd be a fabulous DJ,' but was otherwise a paragon of professionalism, an actual graduate of broadcasting school. When the Radio Authority put some licences up for grabs, I – a go-getter! – had the bright idea of the station presenting live weekly showcases of unsigned (by record companies) would-be recording artists for the attendant publicity. In between the unsigned acts, we would play our favourite stuff from rock's three decades, which would enable me to call the night Raiders Legends.

The first thing we needed was a venue, and I had just the place in mind.

CHAPTER SEVEN

Erotic Emergencies

S ince before the Beatles, the St Moritz in Wardour Street, a claustrophobic subterranean cavern beneath a Swiss restaurant, had been a favourite meeting place of the music biz, probably because it was exactly equidistant from both the Marquee, a club, and The Ship, a pub, rub-a-dub-dub. You would meet friends in the latter at eight, get off your face, and then stagger over to the Marquee at half-nine, either to stand in the ankle-deep spilled lager or, on a less crowded night, to sit at the bar while the featured band performed. Promptly at half-eleven, you would roll or be dragged to the St Moritz to continue to drink until the place closed at three. At four, you would be diagnosed as suffering from cirrhosis of the liver. You'd have died from it by five, and been interred by six, whereupon a new day would dawn in British pop history.

I met with the St Moritz's owner, an irascible little misanthrope who had come, for the same reason that very large men are sometimes nicknamed Tiny, to be known as Sweetie. He agreed to let me present a series of Wednesday night new talent showcases, and I was away.

A couple of nights later, after our traditional station meeting in the Ship, I was sitting with Raiders' manager and a girl into whose knickers he was trying to get with promises of exciting opportunities in broadcasting, when I noticed an attractive bum at the bar. It was part of a toned and tanned bod, pleasingly accessorised with braces and long blond hair. Soon we were chatting. His name was Jonathan, he was the drummer in the extremely popular covers band Vegetarian Haggis, and he had two brain cells to rub together, with many more to spare. Indeed, he was witty and charming.

He asked if I fancied a walk. I said I did, in spite of the fact that I was wearing the provocative footwear that, along with my haughty scowl, would become one of my trademarks. As we approached the Swiss Centre in Leicester Square, he abruptly stopped and asked for a kiss. How endearingly quaint! What sort of St Moritz habitué in tight black trousers and long blond hair *asked*? The idea was simply to grab what you fancied – me rock type, you Jane. For his trouble, he got rather more than a mere kiss.

A few days hence, I visited his flat in Earls Court, and he asked if I'd be his girlfriend. I would, and was, for nearly two years.

During which I got introduced to kink.

It turned out that Jonathan very much liked me to wear very silky stockings when we made love – only slightly less than he liked wearing them himself. It turned out that he also much enjoyed fetish clubs, so we resolved to attend one, even though I lacked the requisite gear. I faked it as best I could in a black hook-and-eye corset top, short, tight skirt, and black boots that covered my gorgeous knees. Jonathan, himself a vision in black leather trousers, apparently liked my outfit, as, finding a secluded corner in the back of the club, he lifted me on to a table, knelt before me, and had at my most intimate part with his tongue. He undid the hooks of my top and led me round for a while with my breasts exposed, and then confiscated my knickers and pulled me down on his lap, scandalising the revellers at the table opposite.

I went to the Ladies, and found it full of gorgeous six-foot sexpots with huge false eyelashes, gigantic hair, pouty lips and penises. One of them asked, very politely, if she could kiss my boots. How, but for the shrill importunings of my bladder, could I have refused? As I made my way back to Jonathan, I reflected on the extraordinary level of mutual respect evident at the club. No bottom-pinching and slobbered come-ons here, boy, no boorishness of any kind. Here, unerring civility and deference.

Not long thereafter, I turned up at Jonathan's flat to discover that he'd hired a video camera for the weekend, with the intention of having something to show our grandchildren if ever they were curious about our erotic interactions back in the late eighties. I dutifully changed into the basque, stockings, and heels I kept at Jonathan's in case of erotic emergencies, but didn't find the filming process much fun – he was forever losing his erection as he leapt up to reposition the camera – at least until I tied him spread-eagled, blindfolded, and gagged to the four posts of the bed. I discovered that I quite fancied having a bloke completely at my mercy, and who could blame me?

In the end, my immaturity was the death of us. Once he'd played a gig, Jonathan, a teetotaller, wanted to go home, slip into his stockings, and put his feet up. I, ten years younger, wanted to bask in the reflected glory of being the girlfriend of a minor pop star, and flirted openly with estimable rock hunks beyond number. I broke Jonathan's heart, then changed my mind and asked him to have me back. He wouldn't.

My dad's elder brother, who'd lived a couple of miles from us during most of my childhood, now died and left his house to my dad, who immediately signed it over to me and Fiona. I moved into the bottom, she into the top, and within three days we could hardly bear the sight of one another. But at least I had Marlin.

On a very cold February night twelve years before, as I walked past a late-night grocery store at 8.30 p.m. on the way to a pub in Shepherd's Bush Green, I'd noticed a thin black dog tied to the grille used to secure the premises at night. Walking back past the store at eleven, I was horrified to see the little dog still there, shivering violently in the cold. She had peed on the ground repeatedly in the interim. Unhooking her chain, I asked the proprietor, who had come out to lock up, whether he knew whom she belonged to. He knew only that she would have to be moved, as he was about to close for the night. I decided to take her home.

A nervous little thing, she spent her first night trembling on my bedroom floor. Next morning I went down to the local police station to report that I'd found her. They told me that if she wasn't claimed within seven days, she would legally be mine. I'd already fallen in love with her, named her Marlin, and determined not to return her in any circumstances to her callous previous owner. Thus began the most precious relationship of my life.

Probably a cross between a lurcher and an alsatian, she was jet black apart from a white patch on her chest and a tiny white tip of hair on her front right paw, and so shiny she gleamed, with huge bat ears, one of which flopped over ever so endearingly. During our long daily walks in Alexandra Park or Highgate Woods, she proved to be an implacable chaser of squirrels and cats, at whom she would launch herself at speeds that left me breathless. When we were out in a pub, she wouldn't be happy unless curled up in my lap, although she was really too big for such babying. She was fiercely protective of me, warning strangers away with a bark much bigger than she was. At night she would lie beside me on the bed, stretch out her legs and give a low sigh of deep contentment.

I longed to have human friends in many lands, though, and placed adverts in foreign newspapers, such as the Saskatoon *Tooning Fork*, and other fancifully named Canadian publications. Given that most Canadian newspapers have readerships that could very easily fit in the upper deck of a London bus,

I expected little, and got it. But then, months later, long after I'd forgotten about having placed the ad, I received a letter and photograph from the apparently clever Mr Stewart Marks of Vancouver, British Columbia, who played keyboards in a New Romantic-style band that was thinking of trying its luck in British Britain. Did I, he asked, have any contacts in the London music business? If there was one thing in the world that I had – I, who had worked for the Musicians' Union, and been one of the leading lights of pirate radio, and presented deserving-but-unsigned bands without number at the St Moritz, and cavorted carnally with the drummer of Vegetarian Haggis – it was contacts in the music biz.

As a teenager, I'd been bewitched by 'Ventura Highway' by the pop group America, so I'd run an ad in an LA paper as well. I heard from a few hundred respondents, mostly madmen who wanted to fly me over to serve as staff concubine at their communes, but also from Dennis, whose photos showed him to be the sort of tall, bronzed, long-blond-haired specimen I'd had in mind. I sent him a photo of me and he phoned, quite unexpectedly. We agreed that it would be fun to meet. I continued promoting my unsigned rock talent nights, now at the Water Rats in King's Cross, and managing the bookshop in Muswell Hill, and saved every penny, dreaming of one day riding through shimmering heat down Ventura Highway in an open-topped car, the wind ruining my coiffure.

Imagine my delight, as my savings swelled at last to the requisite immensity, on learning that my new best friend Jade was romantically entangled with the executive producer of *Home Alone* – who owned a house in the Hollywood Hills, and who was willing to let us look after it for him while he was away on business for three weeks.

As our plane touched down at LAX, I felt as though I'd gone to Heaven. Jade's boyfriend's house turned out to be within easy walking distance of Hollywood Boulevard, where, at Frederick's of Hollywood, we both bought wigs in which to swelter. Having spent her teens in LA getting drooled on by rock types, Jade had loads of old friends who were willing to drive us to Magic Mountain, Disneyland, Universal Studios, and all the rock clubs in their expensive cars.

I had so much fun that it wasn't until ten days before our return flight to London that I remembered Dennis, who turned out to be even more gorgeous than in his photos. When I told him about my Ventura Highway fantasies, he obligingly booked us into a motel on Ventura Boulevard, as it was called in real life. It was eight lanes wide, ugly, and choking with traffic, but our lovemaking was nearly satisfactory, and he showed up at Jade's boyfriend's house the next night on a huge motorbike. Riding behind him, my arms round his lovely taut abdomen, the warm wind in my face, the palm trees flashing by, I felt as though my dream had come true.

When I flew back to London, we burned up the transatlantic phone lines until we realised that the airfare for him to come over would probably be cheaper. Two weeks of bliss followed. And then he began doing the most extraordinary Joe the Woe imitation. Sitting in the pub, he'd accuse me of watching other men, and I'd wind up staring at the floor to keep from provoking him. On our second Saturday night, as I sprayed myself, before heading for the Water Rats, with the perfume he'd bought duty-free on the plane over, he seethed. 'I bought that for you to wear for *me*,' he snarled, 'not other dudes.' Dumbfounded, I invited him to come with me, to ensure that no alien nostrils might detect my scent, but he preferred to stay home and brood.

When I got home, he sniffed me suspiciously, and then suddenly screamed, 'You've been with someone else, haven't you, bitch?' The memory of the abuse I'd suffered at Joe's hands flooded back, and I fled, winding up sobbing on a bench in front of the Baptist church a few hundred yards up the road. After half an hour, I remembered that it was my bloody flat, and returned, gingerly. Denny, nice and warm and comfy on my sofa, had calmed down to the point at which I felt able to tell him he'd have to go. And there went yet another one.

Inspired by my friend Monty Zero, the celebrated Marquee DJ, I began doing live work in addition to my radio show, and was soon the toast of all Western Europe as a result of my regular gig at the Opera on the Green in Shepherd's Bush. But I continued to long for kink, and when I heard that a new club called Torture Garden was about to burst upon the scene, eagerly made plans to attend.

I hadn't been wrong before about the people who attended these things – they really were very much better-behaved than their vanilla counterparts. Once again someone wanted to kiss my feet. I let him. As he got to work, a fetching creature called Jeanette seated herself beside me and struck up a conversation. By and by, I sussed that she was in fact a man, and eagerly accepted her offer of a ride home to my new digs in Muswell Hill. Had any of my new neighbours, finding it hard to sleep, been peeping through their curtains when we arrived, what a spectacle they would have beheld – two gaudy slappers in fetish attire snogging with great enthusiasm.

She rang the next morning, and I excitedly told her to meet me after my gig at the Opera that evening. As the Only Ones brought the evening to a close, I was horrified to realise that the weedy-looking git in a ghastly striped rugby shirt who'd been loitering by the DJ booth through most of the latter half of the evening was Jeanette out of drag. I feigned great regret as I informed him that I'd only just remembered that I needed to wash my hair, and left him standing there looking crestfallen and scandalously ungorgeous.

My appetite for kink was undiminished, though, and in fact so voracious by now that I took the extraordinary step of ringing Joe the Woe, who I'd always suspected had cards he wasn't showing. How else to feel about a man who paints his fingernails black and wears more eyeliner than Brigitte Bardot in her heyday, but won't let you get on top during lovemaking for fear of seeming insufficiently masculine?

I went over to his place and plied him with Bordeaux. After two bottles, he confessed that he'd always fancied the idea of being tied up and flogged. We headed eagerly, if unsteadily, for the bedroom. Lacking handcuffs and chains, I improvised with scarves, but I'd hardly begun walloping him than the whole idea began to strike me as so funny that I began giggling in spite of myself. He joined in, and soon we were in stitches.

Now it can be told, or at least admitted – BDSM is fundamentally pretty hilarious.

CHAPTER EIGHT

I the Duck, and He the Water

Based on my offer of help with contacts, Mr Stewart Marks of Vancouver brought his two fellow band members over, and rented a big house from whose living room window they could nearly reach out and touch Karl Marx's grave in Highgate Cemetery. Over the course of the next five years, he visited me often to brief me on what was going on with his band. Very, very little had gone on to that point, the creative apogee of their career having been a video containing every last cliché of the last days of the New Romantics, but if no one would sign the band, surely some publisher would sign Stewart as a songwriter. He set to work composing songs that Sade would surely want to record, regularly dropping in to keep me posted, never laying a finger on me – great songwriters, like great boxers, must avoid ejaculation like the plague – but at one memorable juncture noticing the famous limbs and appreciatively murmuring, 'Legs!'

I wasn't inconsolable. I didn't rush into my bedroom the moment he left to see if I could determine what it was about my makeup that had made him want to dash off without trying to persuade me to wrap the famous limbs round his narrow back. He was entirely too eccentric for that. He would, when we ventured out together, strike up conversations with anyone, anywhere, at the slightest provocation, and, before they knew what had hit them, he'd have free-associated himself on to a topic very far afield of the one they'd started on. You'd never seen anyone inspire so much perplexed gaping. Some poor old woman queued up for the 83? Stewart would want to know which LP of the Fixx's she found most fab. A French tourist couple photographing the pigeons in Trafalgar Square? Perhaps they would be able to share something fascinating about the native flora of Sri Lanka with him.

Fully five years after Stewart and I originally became penpals, he came over one night to get me up to speed on his new Sade-comeback-smash-to-be and I welcomed him at last into my bedroom as I took to doing whenever his busy composing and demo-recording schedule permitted.

He proposed. I did the only sensible thing, and fled.

Actually, my fleeing had less to do with Stewart's proposal than with the imminence of Guy Fawkes Night. As soon as she heard the first high-pitched whistling rocket of the season, Marlin's eyes would widen with terror and she'd go into a terrible heaving pant that made me worry she'd have a heart attack. In previous years, I'd got her sedatives from the vet, but had hated their effect on her. This year, I resolved that we would spend the night in a town too tiny for fireworks, and found it in the form of Aldeburgh on the Sussex coast.

Windswept and frigid, pitch black at night, the town proved delightfully free of distracting and terrifying revelry, and I phoned Stewart from the phone box on the seafront near my rented cottage to say that I would indeed be his bride. We decided that if the Chelsea register office in the King's Road had been good enough for Mick Jagger and Bianca, it would probably suffice for us too.

Having decided to tie the knot before Christmas, I had, on returning to London, mere weeks to get everything organised, but I am a force of nature, and succeeded. The groom showed up late, but our vows got mumbled. All my friends and family – not a single one of whom, I would eventually learn, lacked grave, grave doubts – managed to look delighted. We were photographed on the famous steps outside the building, the bride all in black, and then proceeded up to Highgate, there to savour a posh vegetarian spread. Whether Karl Marx spun in his nearby grave is a matter of conjecture, but it is well known that my dad gave a speech and that my mum danced with anyone who asked, and a few who didn't.

After spending our wedding night at a hotel in Muswell Hill, I was back in Ruislip and Stewart back in his studio by mid-day the next day, as he had terribly important tracks to record.

Married less than twenty-four hours, and already the wall was full of writing.

If anything, marriage seemed only to make him more singleminded about composing Sade's comeback hit. He took to sleeping in his little demo studio far more often than he slept beside his increasingly frustrated bride. My birthday? He'd have loved to have spent it with me, but was absolutely focused on getting the mix of this new song just right. Christmas? He'd have loved to, but he had an idea for a bass part that simply wouldn't tolerate not being worked out immediately. New Year's Eve? Yom Kippur? The anniversary of our first shag? Sorry: busy.

I didn't take it lying down. I cajoled. I wept. I raged. I howled. I sulked. I threatened. And he wanted very much to talk the situation over in the depth in deserved just as soon as he and Suki, the singer he worked with, had sung the bridge of his new hit-to-be exactly as he'd hoped to hear it sung.

After eighteen months, my whingeing eventually inspired him to drastic action – to take me on a proper honeymoon. He was somehow able to rearrange his busy recording schedule to go to Greece with me for a week. Over the course of our marriage, we'd seen one another once every fortnight. On the long flight from Heathrow to Corfu, it occurred to me that that might not have been such a bad idea, as Stewart decided that it would be hilarious to speak very loudly in a peculiar voice, and I, mortified with embarrassment, came very close to asking the steward for a parachute.

Our hotel wasn't air-conditioned. Had it been a few degrees cooler, one might have described the weather as infernal. We lay side by side on our bed gasping for air, he no doubt thinking about Sade, I cursing myself for having imagined in my wildest dreams that Mr Stewart Marks was a viable candidate for marriage.

It got worse and worse. We went to a restaurant that offered traditional Greek dancing and invited us diners to join in. When they approached our table to add us to the jubilant throng, I realised to my horror that Stewart was hiding underneath.

The next night, we went to a bar. He abruptly excused himself to go and strike up a conversation with a trio of Scandinavian girls seated nearby. For ten minutes, I tried to douse my disgruntlement in *ouzo*, but my disgruntlement would not be doused, and I called to my husband to disentangle himself. He brought the girls back with him. I tried to make small talk, though I'd just as soon have bashed their lovely blonde heads together until they lost consciousness. And you're quite right that my beef wasn't with them. When they and my husband began exchanging email addresses, though, I devoted all my energy to staring daggers at their throats. The girls, more sensitive than he, made their excuses and returned whence they'd come. Five minutes later, Stewart could bear the loss of their company no longer and returned to them, this time for a quarter of an hour.

He came back to me at last, only to remember there was much he hadn't had a chance to relate to his new friends. He knew better than to get up and leave me yet again, though, and was content to shout to them. I kicked him in the leg with all my might. It was the closest we'd come to physical intimacy since leaving London.

We barely spoke on the flight home, and a month later, feeling as despondent as it's possible to feel without disintegrating, I began divorce proceedings.

I thought I'd feel relieved when I got my decree absolute. Instead, I felt devastated. My mum and dad had been married for forty-one years. I'd managed less than two. There was no man in my life, and I'd long since gone off women. I was about to turn forty. I wanted to cry, and God knows I did. A river.

I found hope in an unlikely place – on my computer monitor. There were countless dozens of dating services on the Internet, and I signed up for all of them. You had to compose a little self-description. I flirted with the idea of satire: *Desperate, Lonely, Miserable! Urgently seeking anything in trousers. Please help me!* I came to my senses in the nick of time, and instead concocted what I dared hope was an enticing blend of fact and flirtation. I made clear that the man I hoped to meet would be confident, articulate, intelligent, and gorgeous. Exploiting the miracle of the self-timer, I photographed myself with my digital camera. I uploaded the lot and cried myself to sleep, as had become my custom.

A torrent!

I received more responses than I could read, and quickly found that I didn't want to read most of them. These blokes honestly imagined themselves to be remotely presentable, never mind gorgeous? If so, they were delusional. They'd been whupped with ugly sticks, many of them. Others were so ugly that when they wept, the tears probably tried desperately to scurry back up into their eyes. When they tried to enter ugly contests, the judges said 'Sorry, no professionals.'

Actually, in some cases, I could have got past a respondent's not being Adam Ant if he'd known how to spell, or that there was such a thing as lower-case too, and that it was possible to compose email that WASNT ALL IN UPPER-CASE. I mean, don't misspellings look bad enough when they're not bellowing at you?

I thought of packing it in, and resigning myself to a life of solitude. Then I passed Fiona on the stairs and saw where that resolution would lead, and went anew to my email inbox, which contained a message alerting me to someone new having responded to my UK Matchmaker listing. Fully expecting yet another subliterate eyesore, I clicked the link, and discovered that I'd actually heard from someone whose knuckles probably didn't get painfully scraped if he walked from one end of the road to the other.

Mr Nic Stoker's photograph depicted him in front of gently swaying (I extrapolated) palm trees on a white sand beach. He had unbuttoned his shirt to show off the exemplary tan he seemed to have acquired while frolicking on it, or perhaps just lying there, revelling in his great prosperity. He had perfect white teeth, but nonetheless seemed to be English. He knew how to release the Shift key on his computer keyboard. Confident didn't begin to describe him. He was nothing short of arrogant:

You'll like me. Most women do, and, to dispense
with false humility, why shouldn't they? I'm 36,
Jewish, very fit, as you can see from the photo I've

attached, and the owner of my own very successful, very time-consuming software company, based here in north London, but with an office in Florida. I love good food (and am a gourmet cook), good wine, and stimulating conversation, and am interested in a wide variety of things, from astronomy to zoology. I very much enjoy seeing the latest films, and have an enormous record and CD collection, two of my personal favourites being the American band Journey and our own (or at least Scotland's) Strangeways, of whom far too few people have heard, if you want my opinion. I play tennis and squash and Spanish guitar, sail, and ski. I am a patient, considerate lover, and, if you'll permit my noting it, generously endowed. I am the devoted father of a four-year-old daughter from whose mum I am in the process of getting a divorce.

I feel sure that you won't regret meeting me for a get-acquainted drink, from which we can proceed to dinner if we get on as well as something tells me we will.

I was woozy. I'd thought I might be the only person in Britain who was mad about Strangeways, who sounded like a very eloquent homegrown answer to Journey, whom I also loved. And all the commas were in the right places! And those teeth! And Florida! And I'd been known, in the days before there was a VCR in every home, to decline invitations to go out with friends so I could watch programmes about the Hubble Telescope!

I lay down until the room stopped spinning. I returned to my computer, and then realised, before typing a single character, that I needed to give this more thought. I lay down again. He wasn't my type, not at all. My type didn't have perfect teeth or a tan, and appeared never to have been outdoors in daylight, and was too bony-chested to pose with an unbuttoned shirt. My type played electric, and not Spanish, guitar.

God, was I fed up with my type.

I wrote this response:

God, yes! Please phone me the instant you read this
for directions to my home. I'll leave the door open,
and will be waiting for you in the bedroom, second
door on the right.

I'd learned a thing or two since I'd swooned compliantly at the feet of my first boyfriend Graham the Alpha Male the moment he indicated an interest in me. Re-reading what I'd composed, I thought it might seem a bit overly keen, and produced a second draft.

Thank you for your kind response to my Matchmaker
UK posting. I think we may indeed have something
in common, and will look forward to meeting you for
the drink you propose.

Still too keen, I thought, when I reread it after a brief visit to the loo. This time, I nailed it.

Thank you for your response to my Matchmaker UK
posting. I am willing to meet you for a drink at some
point, but am not sure when, as I am very busy.

Men are so wonderfully predictable, aren't they? Tell them
they can't have it and their arteries start bulging with testosterone
that screams at their brains, 'But you *must* get it, or perish!' Nic
must have been on line, and with his email application open,
as, within 90 seconds of my clicking Send, there he was again,
panting to know if I had ICQ, a programme that enables two
people to send one another digital messages in real time. I did
indeed, and we both got on – and for ten days rarely got off, as
we grew to know one another better and better the fab impersonal
modern way, by typing at one another.

One of my favourite cartoons of the past several years,
by the American artist Piraro, depicts a policeman, behind a
two-way mirror, saying through his microphone to one of four
misshapen dweebs in a police line-up, 'Number 4, step up to
the computer and type the words *I am 6-4, muscular, with thick,
wavy hair*,' while a victimised woman stares balefully at her
monitor beside the sergeant. Which is to say that I knew very
well that the real Mr Nic Stoker might bear heartbreakingly little
resemblance to the witty, urbane bronzed Adonis with perfect
white teeth I'd come to know on line.

For our first face-to-face meeting, I, either a loyal customer
or a woman of impoverished imagination, chose the Ship in
Wardour Street. Arriving early, I ordered a drink, found a
sympathetic-looking table to stand next to, and sipped it. Five
minutes later – right on the dot! – Mr Nic Stoker swaggered

in oozing confidence and affluence and looking not as good as the JPEG he'd transmitted, but even better – if very much shorter than he'd ever let on. Sussing instantly which of the unaccompanied, expectant-looking women in the place was I – no fool, Mr Nic Stoker! – he swaggered towards me, grinning dazzlingly with his perfect teeth and eyeing me up and down in a way that would have got him slapped hard if he'd been a stranger. As it was, I quite liked his cheek. 'Let me take you away from all this,' he murmured sultrily as he kissed my hand, and the next thing I knew, we were in a different bar, in Berwick Street.

The longer we talked, the more I wanted to sweep all our glasses off the table, fling myself down on my back, and pull him atop me. He was extremely self-assured, but not overbearing, and was a gentleman. Not only that, he didn't once pointedly hold up his glass and lick his lips thirstily, as though to send me scurrying to the bar to buy my round. It was obvious that if I so much as put my hand in my pocket, he would break my arm at the elbow. It also became increasingly obvious that he wanted to be atop me on the table as much as I wanted him to. Knowing that I was on the verge of ceasing prematurely to be hard-to-get, I suggested that we move along to the celebrated Soho cabaret Madame Jo-Jo's, my thought being that if anything could get my mind off how much I wanted to stroke Mr Nic Stoker's poker, it would be the good Madame's luscious TV waitresses.

The drinks flowed, as too did our conversation, at least until, at one point, he whispered, 'You know, there's something just a bit odd about these waitresses.' Then I realised he was being mischievous – ironic, even! – and fancied him all the more. His arm found its way round my shoulders. My own hand somehow stayed out of his lap. Magic!

We drove back to his office in Highgate, from which he called me a cab. We embraced. I looked for a desk to sweep everything off and hurl myself down upon backwards. Thank God for the cab, which arrived just as I spotted one. I can tell you nothing about the long ride home. I was so euphoric that the guy could have driven me to Barking.

The moment I awoke the next morning I hurried into the lounge to turn on my computer, and there was a message from him, telling me that he'd loved being with me. Could I meet him for lunch? If so, could I be persuaded to have dinner with him as well? I nearly swooned with pleasure. I nearly ran upstairs and embraced Fiona.

I invited him for dinner at my place a few days later. One thing led to another, and hence into my bedroom. He was good! And I in seventh heaven.

We're a nation of shopkeepers, and I became one of them. Deciding that what the humane women and crossdressers of Harrow really needed, without realising it fully yet, was a shop offering cosmetics manufactured by companies that didn't test their products on animals, I flung open the doors of the misleadingly named Other Nations in November 1996, and the women and crossdressers of Harrow very convincingly pretended not to have noticed. It wasn't until Thursday afternoon that someone finally came in, an elderly Bengali gentleman rather urgently in need of the Gents. And then the deluge. In three months, I sold a whopping £276 worth of cruelty-free cosmetics. I rang the market owner to say that I'd abandoned the idea of being a shopkeeper, delighted all my friends (oh, sure) with Christmas gifts of cruelty-free lipsticks and mascara and blusher, cried myself to sleep four nights running, or at least would have liked to, as it might have made me feel better, and found a job describing traffic conditions on the radio for AA Roadwatch. This had sounded reasonably good fun until I realised that it was half-five in the morning, and not in the afternoon, that they expected me to show up for work in Stanmore, which wasn't exactly round the corner, was it?

The commute was long and the hours brutal; the pay was awful – a whopping £6.50 per hour. I lasted eight months.

Bloodied but unbowed, implacably entrepreneurial, I started a dog-walking and house-sitting business, putting little notices about my availability in every newsagent's window in north-west London. But it turned out that the region's pet owners were in cahoots with its humane women and crossdressers, and the phone just sat there sullenly on my table, mocking me with its muteness.

I consulted my close friends at the Harrow Job Centre, who believed that, with my upmarket accent and engaging personality, I'd be really good at polling the public by telephone, and hooked me up with a local market research company. Four mornings a week, I was to report to an airless, windowless office in Eastcote with a mob of otherwise-unemployables, a great many of whom seemed quite capable of whipping out machine guns on the No. 250 to Watford and mowing down their fellow commuters. I felt as though I'd gone to Hell. But then I actually began making my calls, and felt worse.

I was charged with determining whether anyone in the household were 'on line', as in 'connected to the Internet'. Those who weren't uncomprehending were hostile. You'd have thought I was asking if they frequently suffered from piles. Of the five persons I phoned, two couldn't for love or money be made to understand what I was trying to determine, one called me a cow and hung up on me, one called me something worse than a cow and hung up on me, and one demanded furiously to know who I *really* was. And all this for £5 per hour. It made me regret having packed in traffic reporting.

During the lone 15-minute break permitted per shift, I would rub thighs in the 'staff room' with lumpy matrons in criminally hideous floral print dresses and grey-bearded men in blue anoraks who brought their own egg sandwiches from home. And every day, without fail, their conversation was identical.

'How many this morning, Frank?'

'Fifty-three, Sally. But I must admit I've had me problems with Question 3a.'

Just the thing to cheer me up after endless hours of insults, and of 275 exposures to the Number Unobtainable recording, and the headphones hurting my tiny ears!

Having no clue what to say to my colleagues – had even one of them lain, in the Old Testament sense, with one of Adam & The Ants, or been gobbed on by impatient Eddie & The Hot Rods fans at the Hope and Anchor, or had her shoes licked at a party in Hampstead? – I took to spending my breaks in the loo, sobbing inconsolably.

I couldn't bear it. I would have to leave, even though my

bank would be less than delighted. I had combined credit card debts of many, many thousands of pounds.

I did the only thing I could in the circumstances. I bought myself a £4.90 Travel Card and went into town, specifically to Camden, to meet my dear friend Kim for a great many drinks, and then to enjoy a leisurely £20 cab ride home.

And somewhere between Wembley Park and Finchley Road I had the idea that would transform my life. I knew, from my tentative first explorations of the Worldwide Web, that professional dominatrices often charged their clients more for an hour of verbal abuse and spanking than I was making in a week of polling by telephone. Hadn't submissive men queued up at fetish clubs for the privilege of being allowed to kiss my unusually pretty little feet? Didn't some ex-friends regard me as a domineering bitch who always demanded her own way? Didn't I look good in PVC? And then the train came to an unscheduled and unexplained stop a quarter-mile short of Finchley Road, and sat there and sat there and sat there, and I had no recourse but to listen to half my fellow passengers moaning down their mobiles. I thought no more of domination as a career, but only of how I was now going to be late to the pub at which Kim and I had agreed to meet. In the first three years of our friendship, she hadn't been on time twice. I'd coaxed, cajoled, raged, pleaded, the lot. I'd told her gently, in a moment of impeccable composure, that her chronic lateness made me feel disrespected. Real friends, I said, don't waste one another's time. In moments of severe emotional disarray, I'd told her the same thing at the top of my lungs. On one memorable occasion, on our way half an hour late (because she'd been on the phone to a friend and neglected to bathe and change) to a gig whose support act I'd hoped very much to see, I'd shrieked, 'What did you think it was getting – *earlier*?' and a whole carriageful of our fellow passengers on the Victoria line had guffawed. Finally – finally! – she'd begun to reform, and rarely kept me waiting any more. And now *I* was going to keep *her* waiting. I was absolutely fit to be tied.

I wound up arriving pretty well beside myself twelve minutes late. I apologised profusely, blaming it all on the train, mindful of how many times, in response to blaming her own tardiness on the train, I'd told her that one simply couldn't rely on it, and had whenever possible to leave a bit earlier in anticipation of exactly such problems. She wasn't a bitch about it at all, bless her. 'No worries,' she said over and over again with a big smile, apparently having been watching Australian soaps again.

It was August, and brutally hot, so we took our bottle of wine to one of the tables in front of the place. She hadn't much more news than I. Her bipolar playwright boyfriend had been implacably manic the last couple of weeks, to the tune of working on the four plays he was working on simultaneously for up to sixty hours at a stretch. The problem was, she related, that characters in one play frequently responded to something a character in one of the other plays had said, posing a real challenge for the inattentive reader. As usual, what she was enjoying most was studying yoga. As usual, she wondered if I had changed my mind about taking classes, as she'd been urging me to for years. As usual, I told her that I would seriously consider taking classes when she was able to assure me that no physical exertion was involved. (In a remarkable, if little noted, exhibition of passive aggression, I have scrupulously avoided physical exertion since my first-form PE teacher humiliated me in front of a classful of my peers in 1968.)

It occurred to us nearly simultaneously that the odd couple at the adjacent table had curtailed their own chat to stare at us. The elder, maybe thirty-five, seemingly shared my disinclination to physical exertion, but his had made him puffy. He seemed to have bought his utterly anonymous clothing and shoes at BHS. His much younger chum, on the other hand, was the soul of trendiness, circa 1978, in his spiky bleached blond hair, tight pleather trousers, fashionable eyewear, deafening sweater (on a day on which I, normally the first person in any crowd to detect a chill, was wearing a Lycra vest!), and self-assured smirk. But for the fact that they were making no attempt to conceal their interest in me and Kim, I'd have figured the puffy one to have been paying the trendy for his company.

It turned out that it had been Kim's accent that had first attracted their attention, as they were from very much the same neck of the woods, Puffy from Dewsbury and Trendy from Oldham. Kim, bless her, as personable a daughter of the North as you could ever hope to meet, began immediately to chat up a storm with the unfortunate Puffy. But I'm a Londoner, and pretended to be preoccupied with something across the road as I sipped my wine.

'Bloody sweltering today,' Trendy ventured. I thought of suggesting that he remove his frightful sweater, but was loath to give him even that much encouragement. 'Um,' I replied, without opening my mouth, more fascinated than ever with the human drama I alone could see unfolding on the other side of the street.

'Doesn't get this hot oop where we're from,' he said. It was, I was to understand, three jolly Northerners and I having a drink together now. I didn't bother to answer, and a long moment went by, Kim and Puffy's conversation not fizzling out, as I so hoped it would, but actually picking up steam.

It turned out that Puffy and Kim had both, at different times, drunk at a particular pub in Manchester. What an extraordinarily small world it had become!

'A bit standoffish then, eh?' Trendy attempted, still not getting my attention. 'A typical stuck-up posh bird?'

Trendy took a swig of his lager, ran a hand through his bleached spikes, and tried to pretend that he too was interested in something across the road, but he couldn't manage it, and decided to share his opinions of my feet. 'You know,' he said, pleased with his own impudence, 'I've always thought toenail polish naff. Like, what's the point, you know what I mean?' My scarlet toenails were visible through the open toes of the mules I was wearing because it was so hot.

I hated giving him the satisfaction, but I wasn't about to allow him to insult me, and in that moment, Mistress Chloe was born.

I bent towards him. He eagerly gave me his ear. 'On the contrary, you insolent little twerp,' I whispered. 'The fact is that you very much like everything about my gorgeous feet, including my painted toenails.'

I sat back and reached for my drink. His jaw hung open.

He was not so cheeky now. I was the duck, and he the water.

Puffy and Kim continued to reminisce happily about their childhoods Oop North, so I leaned nearer Trendy anew, this time pulling hard on his earlobe as I whispered into his ear, 'In fact, boy, you find my feet so beautiful that you can't resist kissing them.'

It was my turn to be slackjawed with amazement, as he actually reached down for my ankle and began to lift my foot. But I pulled it away. 'No,' I scolded him. 'You're to get down on to the floor and kiss them properly.' And as God is my witness, he slid from his chair and got on his knees beside me, looked around to assess the extent of his imminent humiliation, sighed, and bent forward to do as he'd been told.

'Matthew,' his friend guffawed, 'what on earth are you doing down there, son?'

Licking his Mistress's gorgeous feet was what.

'For Christ's sake, Matt. You're embarrassing me,' Puffy said, reaching for his drink. But Matthew's will was no longer his own. And I was holding his face to my left foot by pressing down on the back of his head with my right.

'Enjoy it,' Kim, getting right into the spirit of the moment, urged Puffy. 'You won't often see this sort of thing back in Dewsbury.'

I took my foot off the back of Matthew's head and pulled him back into his chair by the ear. He couldn't look at his mate, and certainly not at me. Or perhaps I should say Me. He was breathless with excitement. As Kim, correctly sensing that I might want her to, re-engaged the mortified Puffy, I leaned yet again to whisper into the formerly impudent lad's prolifically pierced ear. 'You're nothing but a cheap little tart, aren't you, boy? A cheap, disgusting little cocksucker.'

'Yes, Mistress,' he said, and I felt God's pleasure.

'Repeat it to Me,' I demanded.

'I'm a cheap, disgusting little cocksucker, Mistress.'

I heard the most blood-chillingly diabolical laugh come out of me, pure contempt rendered as sound. It thrilled me. It thrilled him.

'Again,' I demanded.

'I'm a cheap, disgusting little cocksucker, Mistress.'

It occurred to me that I shouldn't allow him to refer to himself as *I*. It was prideful, vainglorious, utterly inappropriate for one who existed only for his Mistress's amusement.

Where was all this stuff *coming* from?

I didn't know, and didn't need to. All I knew for sure was that I had a new trick up my sleeve. Was I going to spend my days polling the great unwashed public about their Internet use, or get up barbarically early to describe traffic conditions? I thought not.

I stood, trusting that Kim would understand what I was about to do. 'We're going,' I announced. There was no way to end this epochal moment other than for me to vanish in a wink. While Kim quickly took a last sip of her wine, poor little smitten, utterly deflated Matthew produced a ballpoint pen and frantically scrawled a phone number on his napkin. 'Please, Mistress,' he said, standing. 'Please do call your cheap little tart.'

'Not bloody likely,' I sniffed, every syllable dripping disdain. And then I was gone.

*   *   *

'Take a chill pill,' Kim, who really did watch too many American, as well as Australian, sitcoms, laughed as we sat down at the bistro round the corner. I was trembling with excitement, beside myself with the exhilaration of what I'd just done.

'But did you see his face?' I demanded excitedly. 'Did you *see* it?'

'I saw it,' she laughed, 'but I wasn't sure I could believe my eyes. All you needed was a black leather corset and a whip and you could have been one of those whatsits.'

'Exactly!' I said, feeling gigantically . . . *empowered.*

Let others poll the great unwashed. My destiny was unmistakable.

I got in at a few minutes before midnight and immediately went on line. I found the home pages of around a dozen professional dominatrices, nine in the UK, two in the States, and an Australian, who seemed to know what they were doing, and emailed all of them saying that I was about to start my own practice, if you will, in London, and that I would very much appreciate whatever advice they might be able to offer. Then I tracked down one who wasn't especially gorgeous or literate or tasteful, but who seemed to be based in nearby Harrow, and emailed to ask if I might be able to hire her premises.

I retired, couldn't get to sleep, and decided to teach myself Web design. But wait. First I would need photos of myself. I took some with the little digital camera. I wore a black PVC minidress I'd bought years before to wear to the fetish clubs Koinneach took me to and some thigh-high black boots with lamentably sensible heels.

I found a site about making your own Web page. It said that one of the best ways to learn HTML, which I gathered to be somehow integral to the process, was by copying some existing code and substituting your own text and photos. Doing so turned out to be rather fun, and by daybreak I'd put together a page that in no way appeared to be the handiwork of some smug ponytailed new media type in the West End, but which at the same time was certainly no worse than what a large percentage of professional dominatrices offered.

Daybreak! It dawned on me that I'd been up all night. And yes, pun intended.

I'd only just begun. Now, according to my research, I had to submit my site to all the big search engines, a task that, in terms of fun, wound up ranking well, well below wiping the stupid self-assured smirk off Trendy's face.

The postman put the morning's post through the letterbox. It was time that Mistress Chloe got to bed.

CHAPTER NINE

Bucking Like a Bronco, Flopping Like a Flounder

Two evenings hence, I met up with Ian, a friend since my days at ITV. Around the eighth year of our friendship, he'd confessed in a state of extreme inebriation that he'd always secretly fancied me. Perhaps four years after that, in a state of even greater inebriation, he'd confided that he had for years enjoyed fantasies of being sexually dominated by the putative pop singer Siouxsie of Banshees fame. I thought he might be just the bloke to talk to about my exciting new prospects.

We met, as we had countless hundreds of thousands of times over the years, at the Ship, had a couple of drinks, and headed for the Pasta Express in Greek Street. We ordered. As he does so often – understandably, in view of the fact that without him the British brewing industry would collapse – Ian needed the Gents.

As I waited for him, I became aware of a pair of young hoorays in loosened ties watching me from their own table. I reflexively looked away. But then I remembered who I had become two nights before in Camden, and beckoned them. They looked at one another and then back at me. Each pointed at himself as though to make sure he was the one I meant. I indicated which of the two I wanted, and checked myself in my compact mirror as he straightened his tie and came over. When he arrived, I ignored him for a long moment. He finally said, 'You wanted me to come over?'

I suffered a moment's grave uncertainty. I was in danger of making a perfect prat of myself, but I had to let this play out. I snapped my compact closed, took a sip of my wine, and only then glowered up at him, exuding hauteur. 'You will not dare to speak until spoken to.'

His eyebrows shot up. He didn't know quite what to do. He turned back to his mate, but his mate was in no position to help. He cleared his throat and said, 'Yes, ma'am.' It was working! I took another sip of wine and held the glass up to the light at some length, pointedly ignoring him. He shuffled his feet. 'Be still, boy,' I snapped. He was motionless, as he remained even after Ian returned, whereupon I waved him away. When he didn't respond, I glowered at him again and said, 'You are dismissed, boy. Off with you.'

He stammered his assent and left us.

'May I ask what that was all about?' Ian marvelled.

'I'm not sure exactly what it is,' I told him, more delighted
with myself than it would have been gracious to express, 'but I
seem to have it. Do you fancy Mistress Chloe as a name for a
dominatrix?'

The next day I put an advert in the Harrow *Observer*: 'Been a
naughty boy? Beautiful governess will administer the harsh dis-
cipline you require.' At the end, I offered my mobile number.

I got on line and was thrilled to discover that I had an email
from a guy in Glasgow who called himself Billy Dogsbody and
apparently ran a Website that listed all the UK's dominant
women. I was amused by his capitalising You, but not i, and
thrilled by his addressing me (Me!) as Mistress. My delight
wasn't diminished by his having spelled every other word
wrong, and by his syntax being that of someone who had
had to leave school for the mines at age six. He asked that
I supply him with a small gallery (*galry*) of photos. He was
especially keen to see some of me in rubber. I hadn't any.

I found the Website of a boutique in Amsterdam that offered
a line of extremely sexy rubber clothing at extremely high prices.
Mindful that you have to spend money to make money, and
having not yet maxed one of my credit cards, I ordered a black
latex hobble skirt, and then hurried to my job phoning people
to ask if they were on line.

There were a couple of times that afternoon when, after
being called a stupid cow, I very much wanted to become
Mistress Chloe, and finally did so after this one yobbo crossed
the line. I began the conversation as I began all of them,
apologising for disturbing him, assuring him that I would take

no more than ninety seconds of his time, and asking if he owned a personal computer.

'No, darling,' he slobbered, his knuckles almost certainly touching the dirt floor of the hovel in which he undoubtedly lived. 'I ain't got no fucking personal computer, darling. I got summink loads better. Between me legs.' Someone guffawed moronically in the background.

I neither said anything nor broke the connection. He was duly confounded. 'You there, darling?' he finally asked.

'Very much so, boy,' I finally answered icily. 'Here and waiting for the abject apology that you will offer before I determine if the next person on my list is also subhuman riffraff.'

Utter silence at his end. And then he nearly whispered, 'Cor, you've really got a very sexy voice, ain't you?'

'That's hardly for you to say, boy. On your knees.'

There was fear in his voice now. He was trying not to be overheard. 'I can't do that. Me mate Stan is right in the next room.'

'On! Your! Knees!' I said, not loudly, but very, very authoritatively.

'Fucking hell,' he said. I could tell that he was having a very hard time trying, with his abnormally small brain, to figure out if he could manage it without Stan coming in and discovering him. I hung up on him and bit my lip to keep from exploding into laughter. I still wasn't sure what it was, but I was becoming more convinced by the hour that I had it. To burn.

On the bus home, I computed that I had spent approximately eighteen times more on my rubber hobble skirt than

I'd earned that day. But wasn't my ship obviously just about to come in? Hadn't I received a response to my emails to both BitchGoddess.com, one of the biggest American domina showcases on the Web, and WormWilliam.com, its Australian counterpart? And hadn't both agreed not only to list me, but to offer links back to my own little site? The money would soon pour in. Of this there could be no question.

I needed some gear: a riding crop, a paddle, some handcuffs, a leash and collar, a blindfold, a tawse, that sort of thing. I returned for it to Camden, the scene of my breakthrough triumph, wary in case I would have to buy it from a leering wide boy who'd want to know exactly what I had in mind. But my fears were unfounded. I was able to buy most of what I wanted at a little shop presided over by a timid Gothic waif in purple eyeshadow and lipstick.

On the train home, Mistress Chloe received her first response to the Harrow *Observer* advert, but it was her alter ego, Claire Mansfield, who answered in her characteristic upbeat way, and I don't think the punter ever got over it. At first, he was sure he must have got the wrong number, as he'd been trying to reach the beautiful strict governess. As best I could, I summoned the voice I'd earlier used on the phone to Stan's yobbo mate, but couldn't do it well, as I was surrounded by fellow commuters. I told the guy that he should ring me back in twenty minutes' time.

My phone rang two minutes after I got off the train. I answered it fully in character this time, oozing imperiousness. And this time, of course, it was Fiona. 'What's your *problem*?' she wanted to know. She'd rung to whinge about there being no toilet paper in the house. As though she'd bought a roll since we'd moved in together! I told her I was expecting an important call, and that, if she found herself without toilet paper, there were shops within just a few minutes' walk that would be only too delighted to sell her some. 'Right,' she said, bitterly. 'For bloody half again what Tesco sells it for.'

Honestly, how not to adore such a sibling?

The punter rang back. I decided that nothing would work but for me to answer my mobile in a neutral tone that would neither put off prospective punters nor alarm family and friends. The punter was rather more nervous this time than the first, and my being haughty seemed only to make it worse, so I toned it down in a hurry. His particular interest was in being made to wear a pink satin dress, white stockings, and ballet shoes that he would bring with him, and then to be verbally assaulted. I was a bit disappointed that I wouldn't get to use my very serviceable new riding crop, paddle, handcuffs, or leash and collar, but his not balking when I informed him that an hour of my time would cost him £125 more than made up for it.

'May I know where Mistress's dungeon is?' he asked.

Whoops. I'd got well, well ahead of myself, hadn't I? 'For an extremely naughty little girl like you,' I said, making it up as I went along, 'no dungeon is required. I will see you in my . . . in the flat I'm house-sitting for a friend.' We agreed that he would come over at three on Saturday afternoon.

I got on line. Things were moving wonderfully quickly now. Both Bitch Goddess and Worm William had indeed listed me, and I had no fewer than four emails from blokes who'd seen the listings. Two of them were subliterate morons, one of whom wanted to fuck my shoes. The other wanted me to walk on him while wearing extremely high heels – a jolly good trick, I thought.

The third, from someone who called himself subnoel, looked very much more intriguing. It was literate, even eloquent, from a businessman in Lincolnshire who said that he'd fantasised for years about signing himself over body and soul to a beautiful Mistress who would exploit him ruthlessly. 'I fully expect You to plunder my bank account without a moment's hesitation,' he wrote. 'Indeed, Your doing so will be very liberating for me, even exhilarating. I implore You, Mistress, to send me a binding legal contract that i will eagerly and promptly send back signed and notarised, along with a cheque in any amount You specify, limited only by the combined balance of my several accounts, which at this writing total some £1.25 million.'

I'd won the lottery. Forty-eight hours a dominatrix, and already a millionaire! I reread the email, and then reread it again. There seemed to be no catches. I was rich! I felt like dashing upstairs and embracing Fiona. *No toilet rolls, little sister? Here's a thousand quid. Have some delivered!* I broke open the bottle of Dom Perignon I'd been saving for a special occasion and had a couple of glasses while I reread the email again.

But how to respond? If I immediately accepted his offer, would subnoel think me too easy, and retract it? Indeed, should I allow a few days to pass before I responded, in the same way that, as a teenager, I'd forced myself to allow the phone to ring multiple times before answering? Was subnoel the sort who thrived on abuse, and, if so, would I not be cutting my own throat by not telling him to piss off?

It was maddening.

My third glass of champagne made everything clearer. I laboured over my response, which I decided to transmit in twenty-four hours' time, no less diligently than I might have over a *haiku*. Starting a sentence with a lower-case letter went very much against my grain, but I forced myself:

> your offer interests me, worm. Naturally, I receive
> such offers quite regularly, and a good many of them
> turn out to be bogus. To corroborate your sincerity,
> you shall send a money order to the amount of £1000
> to me at the following address.

This done, I turned my attention to my fourth and last email, from the 'creative director' of Bitch Goddess, who seemed rather too aware of his own wit. 'Dear Madam,' it read, 'We propose to feature you in the Web's premier on line magazine of dazzling dominant divas and the whimpering weaklings who worship them. Kindly advise of your interest.' I went to the site whose URL the message included, and found it quite beautiful – if, like the email, rather too fond of the sound of its own unrelentingly snide voice. Which isn't to deny that it made me laugh out loud with, for instance: 'Fall prey to The Subtle Allure of Goddess Sondra of Reno [said personage, according to the photograph on the first page of her feature, being a bleached blonde with preposterous false breasts, holding her legs wide open for the camera]. She wishes she'd been born rich rather than good-looking. We have no comment!'

Exploring further, I discovered this preface to a feature on

a toothy Australian who made my own least literate correspondents look in comparison like Martin Amis:

> It is our custom at Bitch Goddess to copy edit
> our dominatrix profiles, to repair grammatical and
> spelling miscues, and so on. But in the case of our
> exquisite Bitch of the Month for the last week in
> June, we left the text that She submitted untouched,
> feeling that in its pristine state, it conveys things
> about this remarkable dominant beauty that would
> otherwise have been lost. (My own favorite part is
> about how she restricts her reading to 'manly women
> magazines'.)

Amused but wary that they might turn their sarcasm on me,
I dashed off a brief, haughty response asking what would be
required, and then devoted the balance of the evening to trying
to decide whether I should buy a holiday home in the South of
France or the West Country with subnoel's money. Polishing
off the champagne single-handedly, I decided on the former and
went to bed very happy indeed, little imagining at that point that
subnoel was very much an archetype.

Any professional dominatrix will tell you that there are
hundreds of such characters out there who routinely offer her
the moon, and then are never heard from again. My guess is
that promising to turn over their bank accounts for ruthless
exploitation is the only way they can get themselves sufficiently
rigid to wank.

*   *   *

By the time Saturday afternoon rolled round, I wasn't just a bundle of nerves, but a lorryful. What if my first punter turned out to be a stalker, and twigged that I wasn't house-sitting at all? What if, every time I walked Marlin or had to go to Tesco, he was hiding behind a hedge on the other side of the road?

There was apt to be a very great deal of difference between allowing a submissive man at a fetish club to kiss my feet and making this guy feel that he was getting his £125 worth. What if he didn't think I was giving good value for money and demanded it back, and, when I refused to give it to him, started grabbing my personal effects? It isn't as though I'd be able to holler for a neighbour. And a great whopping lot of good the neighbours had been a couple of months earlier when the cab driver who'd driven me home from my mate Angela's place in Brockley, South London, had tried to overcharge me by ten quid and then begun screaming bloody murder and pounding on the windows when I paid him what he should have charged and went into the house. Oh, they'd demonstrated themselves dab hands at peeking out from behind their lace curtains. And yes, I have got very far afield of the subject at hand. And I apologise.

And I had no proper shoes! I could have worn my thigh-high boots to go shopping at the Pinner Tesco. What if my punter were a high heel fetishist? Why hadn't it occurred to me to ask if he had any special wardrobe requests?

I wouldn't answer the door when he came. Yes, that's what I'd do. If Fiona demanded to know what was going on, I'd tell her it was the mad cab driver come back to haunt me, and assure her that I'd handle it in my own way, and she could get back to her telly and cigarettes.

And my dad! Jesus, I'd forgotten all about my dad. He had his own key to the place, and occasionally let himself in when he needed to get something out of the shed in the garden.

I broke open a bottle of wine and had two glasses in less time than it would have taken most people, in more serene circumstances, to remove the cork. I felt slightly calmer, at least until it occurred to me that I wouldn't be able to claim very credibly that I was house-sitting if there were pictures of me and my friends all over the room. I collected them all and hid them in the cabinet on which my TV sits. Thinking about how much money I stood to make strengthened my resolve, and a third glass of wine strengthened it further. I put on my makeup. It was five minutes to three.

And then five minutes after. And then seven. All that aggravation for nothing! What a little fool I'd been to put myself through such . . .

The doorbell rang. I was immobilised by terror. I didn't breathe for fear of his hearing me. Days passed. Weeks. Or a few seconds. The doorbell again. Quite extraordinary, how a doorbell can sound so much more insistent the second time it's rung. The spirit was willing – not keen, mind you, but willing – but the body refused. Only Fiona hollering got me off the sofa. *I am putting one foot in front of the other, left and then right, and then* . . . The doorbell again!

'Oi!' Fiona yelled. She had long found it amusing to express annoyance in the accent of the bovver boy. I was at the door, and turning the knob, and opening it, and eye to eye with a wizened little Asian chappie of around forty who looked even more frightened than I. He immediately averted his eyes. I loved him for that, but there was no trace of gratitude in what I heard coming out of my own mouth. 'Did you not think that ringing once was sufficient, boy?' I demanded. 'Did you imagine that I would leap up immediately?'

'I'm sorry, madam,' he said, tremulously. He was shaking visibly. I loved him for that too.

I grabbed him by the ear and pulled him into the house. I shoved him into the lounge and told him to put down his bag and present My 'tribute'. (I knew from the Internet that we professional dominatrices refer to our hourly fee as a tribute.) He produced his wallet and removed a £100 note, two tens, and a fiver. I was so giddy with excitement that I nearly didn't think to take them from him, and to order him on to his hands and knees. I stuck the money between the pages of *TV Choice*, sat down, crossed My legs as noisily as possible, and stared at him silently for a long moment. His breathing was audible.

I had him remove his shoes and clothing, stack everything neatly, and bring Me his bag in his teeth. It contained his dress, stockings, and shoes.

Another quandary. Do I punish him by making him put those things on, or is that his reward? Every step of the way, I was finding the whole process a great deal trickier than I'd ever realised. But then it occurred to Me that, if My tone were sufficiently disdainful, I could simply ask him.

It worked. Punishment.

'Perhaps we should revisit the issue of your having had the effrontery to ring My doorbell not just once, which would have been perfectly sufficient, but three times. I think you need to be punished severely for that, don't you, boy?'

God, I was good at this stuff. The poor sod was fully erect
and squirming with excitement. 'Yes, Mistress, very severely
indeed.'

'Put on the stockings and shoes for Mistress, worm. Let's
see what a sexy little tart you can be.'

He gasped with excitement, but made no move to reply. I
got up and walked over to him. I stepped lightly on one of his
hands and demanded an explanation for his balkiness.

'Not while You're watching, please, Mistress.'

And thus it came to pass that I had to evacuate my own
lounge so that a wizened little Asian completely unknown to
me as recently as ten minutes before could change unobserved
into a pink satin dress, white stockings, and ballet shoes. I hated
the idea of his being alone in there with my CD collection and
computer.

He looked silly beyond describing in drag and brazen
erection, but my instinct was that I should pretend otherwise,
and I was right. My telling him what a sexy little tart he was
got him breathing very loudly again with excitement.

And then the phone rang. And rang again. And the answer
machine came on, with my own inimitable voice, not some
friend's, inviting the caller to leave a message. It was my old
boss Mick from Raiders FM, and he was apparently intent on
leaving a message that would fill up the whole tape. 'Hello,
Claire,' he began, blowing my cover a little further. I thought
I saw a trace of a smirk on my Asian's tiny features as I stepped
quickly across the room to turn it off.

I told him to move nearer the wall and to lie on his back.
I leaned against the wall and held my foot an inch above his

face. 'Lick, little tart.' He licked, and with great enthusiasm. 'What a brazen little whore you are,' I said, inducing more rapturous squirming, 'what a shameless slag.' His licking wasn't just enthusiastic now, but downright feverish.

And here came all 180 pounds of Fiona down the stairs, loudly. She stopped right outside the door. 'Claire?' She tapped impatiently. 'I was thinking of going to Tesco. Is there anything I can get you?' The one time in all the years we've lived together that she makes this offer.

'No. Thanks.' This delivered in my best no-more-need-be-said tone.

I could hear her opening the front door, but then she came back. 'Are you sure, Claire? I feel bad about being the one who always has to borrow things. There must be something I can get for you.'

'No! Thank you!' You could have heard me at Tesco.

The front door closed. She seemed to have gone, but the little slag wasn't licking any more, and his willie was wilting. He was pouting unashamedly. Clearly on disaster's brink, I did the only thing I could think of – kicked him (gently) in the balls. 'Did I tell you to stop licking, you disgusting little tart?'

In the long moment that he took to think it over, I envisaged myself growing old and bitter phoning reluctant members of the British public to ask them questions that confused and infuriated them. And then he resumed licking, holding my foot with one hand while he stroked himself with the other.

I got more abusive, more graphic. I accused him of being a craven little cocksucker, and told him that, in anticipation of his visit, I'd invited a gang of labourers I'd spoken to the previous afternoon over for blow jobs. He was absolutely in ecstasy.

And about to come.

Right there in my lounge. With nothing but his hand to catch it in.

Another dilemma, in other words. Also, should I let him finish, confident that he'd then piss off early, I with my £125 already in hand, or should I try to keep him excited for the remaining thirty-five minutes that he'd paid for?

'You will ejaculate for Mistress now, bitch,' I commanded, 'keeping in mind that you're going to lick up anything you don't catch.'

God, did he adore *that*! He bucked like a bronco, flopped like a flounder. I'd never known a man to enjoy his orgasm so much.

As best I could determine, he'd caught it all, but what was he supposed to do with it now? I wasn't going to let him use the toilet, as he'd have to go upstairs to do so, and Fiona had been known to head for Tesco, only to find the prospect too daunting a few blocks from our driveway, and suddenly turn back. I would not have the two of them meeting on the stairs. Nor would I have him in my kitchen.

'Eat it,' I said with grave reservations, having no recourse. He obeyed with alarming enthusiasm.

'Well,' I said impatiently, sitting down.

'Yes,' he agreed sheepishly. 'Well.'

'You've had a good time, have you, boy?'

'Marvellous, Mistress. Brilliant.'

'Perhaps you should change back then?'

'Yes, Mistress.' Well, that was a relief, though he clearly expected me to vacate the room again. Pleased with the prospect that he would soon leave, I obliged.

He changed very quickly and knocked on my bedroom door, which I found invasive. 'I'll be going then,' he said, almost as though he expected me to try to stop him.

'Jolly good,' I heard myself reply. I never say *jolly good*, and felt a prat.

He left without meeting either Fiona or my dad. There were no semen stains on my carpet. I was £125 pounds richer. When I found proper premises and didn't have to spend the whole session worrying, I could envisage myself rather enjoying this.

I changed out of my nominal fetish gear, returned to the lounge, and switched on the telly. I picked up my *TV Choice* and realised that £125 should have fallen from it.

The devious little rotter!

I dashed outside. There was no sign of him. I leapt in my car and drove round the neighbourhood for a quarter of an hour. I drove up to the tube station. No trace of him, not anywhere.

I remembered my first night at Pizza Hut, when, just before the public poured in, the manager announced that the whole first night was on the house. 'Priming the pump, like,' he'd said. I told myself that's what I'd just done – primed the pump. And hadn't the lesson I'd learned been priceless?

I didn't believe myself for a second.

CHAPTER TEN

Talking to the Unhappily Fat

I didn't allow myself the time to be despondent. Instead, I got on line and emailed a couple of dozen London-based dominatrices to ask politely if I might be able to rent premises from them. It was almost like phoning the public at large to ask if they were on line. Fifteen of the two dozen didn't respond at all. Six others responded as though annoyed by my enquiry. Of those, five seemed to have had to leave school at around ten. (Couldn't they, I wondered, at least get a literate slave to handle correspondence for them?) The sixth wasn't half fed up with enquiries like mine. *Well, you've got me sussed, Madam. I thought I could get away with being part of the international conspiracy to annoy you, but you were too clever.*

I received an email from the cheeky Yank proprietor of Bitch Goddess. He was pleased with the responses I'd sent him to his Bitch of the Month questionnaire, but dissatisfied with the photos I'd provided. 'These look,' he wrote, 'as though you took them yourself with a digital camera.' Clever bastard. 'And you've got to get yourself some decent shoes. Those in the photos look like dilettante shoes.' I couldn't reasonably have expected him to know about my countless thousands of pounds of credit card debt. On the other hand, I might reasonably have expected him to wait until I solicited his opinion. Americans.

I asked Nic if he'd photograph me. He found the idea sexy. I told him I didn't have any appropriate footwear. He asked what size I wore. I dared to imagine that he'd go into Soho and get me something fabulous.

Such was not the case. When I turned up at his flat a couple of evenings later, I discovered that what he'd done was borrow a pair of very hookerish translucent platform sandals from his sister, whose feet were obviously very much less petite than my own. That was the bad news, the good being that he did indeed find photographing me scowling haughtily most arousing. We hadn't gone at it so long or with such fervour since our fifth date. Afterwards, in an uncharacteristically candid mood, he confessed that he'd been excited by the idea of humbling with his cock the vision of hauteur he'd seen through his viewfinder.

I emailed the new photos to America. 'These are better,' sniffed the cheeky Yank. 'But I can't help but wonder if they wouldn't be better still if you'd worn shoes that weren't three sizes too big.' I had it coming – but was nonetheless beginning to develop a major disliking for him.

I finally heard back from three London mistresses who said they might be able to help out with premises. Of those three, two immediately disappeared off the face of the earth – or at least stopped responding to my emails. And Mistress Jessica of north London said she did indeed know a place that I might be able to use, but had a family health crisis to contend with, and couldn't predict when she might be able to act as go-between.

I couldn't afford to wait. I began phoning round to see if anyone had any kind of space I might be able to convert into a play area. 'Oh, sure,' my friend The Lovely Sally said. 'Why not use one of our guest bedrooms? And then if you fancy some fresh air between sessions, you can go riding on our polo field.' It was very much my week to be the target of sarcasm.

But wait. The extremely unlikely Joe the Woe surprised me by revealing that he'd consider letting me use the utility room of the big ramshackle house he rented in highest High Barnet. It was at the end of the Northern line, half an hour from the West End on a very good day, and commonly surrounded by fifty yards of mud in every direction. But it was either that or do a Fiona and sit gnashing my teeth while my phone and power were shut off for non-payment, and leering thugs congregated outside my door to carry away my furniture.

I drove up to High Barnet to have a look at the place. Full of dust and cobwebs and a washing machine that probably hadn't worked since the Profumo scandal, it pretty nearly inspired me to burst into tears. Could we at least relocate the ancient washing

machine, I asked the Woe. 'Why not?' he said. 'We could take
it up to my bedroom. Or how about the middle of the lounge?'
In fact, the ancient washing machine belonged to the landlord,
who didn't want anything moved. I decided to look on it as a
wonderful test of my ingenuity. I pictured myself telling slaves
that, if they were impudent, I would make them put their heads
in it and turn it on. 'No, Mistress, *please* – not the heavy duty
cycle!' I was unable to make myself chuckle.

I was certainly in no position to buy proper dungeon
furniture, and would have to think more in terms of ambience.
I bought several gallons of matte black paint, and some black
velvet to drape from the walls, and a second-hand rattan chair
and table that I envisaged spray-painting either black or gold,
and some candelabra. I wanted to cry.

All those gallons of matte black paint, and all those walls
crying out for it, and I so disinclined – I very much dislike
painting in spite of one of my A levels being in art. I had
begun to receive two or three emails from submissive male
correspondents every day lately, and it occurred to me that I
might be able to induce some of them up to the Hertfordshire
border to paint while I nibbled vegetarian crudités and called
them awful names.

I wrote to Frederick, who had sent no fewer than three
emails pleading for the opportunity to be my house slave. I
heard from him no more. I tried Bernard, who had claimed
that even cleaning my toilet would be a great honour for him,
provided I allowed him to wear a rubber maid's outfit and
addressed him as Bernadette. He informed me – rather huffily,
I thought – that his arthritis precluded his raising his arms high

enough to paint effectively, and that painting wasn't the sort of thing a mistress ought to have her maid doing anyway.

I confessed my frustration to the cheeky Yank. 'Let me see what I can do,' he said, a bit cryptically, and proceeded to get me a painter, christopher, who emailed to say that he was at my disposal.

I wouldn't let the cheeky Yank off the hook until he'd explained how he'd done it. He was typically flippant and evasive. I wouldn't stop demanding an explanation, though, and eventually he caved in. It turned out that, in the guise of Lady Caroline, gorgeous dominant bitch, he'd been corresponding with submissive men for years.

'You poor twisted sod,' I emailed back. But it turned out there was a definite method to his madness. Browbeating his/Her correspondents mercilessly, he/She regularly induced them to send gifts of shoes and boots and expensive fetishwear. The photographs that inspired this largesse were actually of his girlfriend, the great irony being that she, whom he ruefully described as the well-scrubbed natural type, modelled her bounty for him only with the greatest reluctance. Poor christopher had been one of those who'd written to Lady Caroline to promise his undying devotion.

I died laughing and emailed back to ask the cheeky Yank if he didn't have grave misgivings about preying on the unsuspecting. He wasn't chastened in the slightest. 'The most potent sexual organ,' he responded, 'is the mind. Lady Caroline writes really good email, and stimulates these guys' imagination. It's hardly as though they're not getting something in return for their gifts.' I wrote back to tell him he'd missed his calling, not being a spokesman for Moskowitz Shoes. To which he responded with an email noting that christopher, who seemed to have Self-Esteem Issues (capitals mine, American psychobabble his) seemed the sort to thrive on mistreatment. His hunch was that the more awful I was to the poor devil, the harder he was likely to work.

I emailed the poor devil and told him to come up the following afternoon with a roller, a roller tray, and some brushes. He did so, arriving right on the dot. He was in his mid-forties, very skinny, but with a little round belly, and wore his hair, which was struggling unsuccessfully to remain brown, in a ponytail. I confiscated his clothing, in the process discovering that he had hairy shoulders, so he wouldn't try to duck out prematurely, and left him to paint the utility room while I went into the house proper to chat with the Woe, who was impressed with how glamorously I'd dressed for the occasion, and with how much initiative I was showing. But it wasn't all right with him for me to lock christopher in the utility room with a bucket to pee in and come back in a few hours. What if there were a fire?

Around two and a half hours after christopher arrived, I went back out to the utility room to give him some verbal abuse for his trouble, and to dismiss him. He'd obviously worked hard, and was incredulous that I was already sending him on his way. 'You know, boy,' I said, very much enjoying his cowering, 'one could almost get the impression that you're arguing with Me.' I reached round and yanked his ponytail, making him whimper. I told him that he would remain on call, and that I was likely to summon him again in the next seventy-two hours. He hadn't the spine to resist.

By the following morning, he'd worked up his courage, and sent me a very disgruntled email complaining about having driven up all the way from Folkestone, intent on working long and hard for me, only to be sent home after two and a half hours. And he'd run out of petrol on the motorway, and had got drenched, and apparently had had a perfectly miserable time of it.

I felt a perfect bitch, and emailed the cheeky Yank to demand why he hadn't seen fit to reveal the great distance the poor devil had had to come. It was several hours before he read it, as he lived in San Francisco, and was no doubt sound asleep, dreaming of the expensive fetishwear he'd get unsuspecting innocents to send his balky girlfriend.

His response belied his being the submissive I'd assumed him to be. 'Listen, girlfriend,' he wrote, 'I have no more idea of where Folkestone is than you have of where Guerneville is. And how could I have known that you'd send him away so quickly? A little graciousness – there's the ticket!' Thoroughly piqued, I deleted him from my Outlook Express address book and composed a brief expression of apology for poor christopher. Another day went by, and I inched ever nearer to financial ruin.

I got an email from Goddess Louise, but had written to so many mistresses that I'd forgotten who was who. I revisited her site, which had no photographs, but only Olivia de Bernardinis renderings of Bettie Page, at least until you reached the Foot Worship page, on which no fewer than eighteen pictures of the goddess's meticulously pedicured tootsies were on display.

I went down to Kennington. The moment she opened the door, I realised why she might have hesitated to show herself. She could have got through it only if lavishly greased, and with the help of a tractor. She weighed twenty stone if she weighed an ounce, and, at around four foot eleven, was as big in any direction as in any other. Which was certainly a pity, as she had some of the most gorgeous smooth pale skin I'd ever seen, and extraordinarily glossy black hair of the sort that one often sees being swung in slow motion in adverts for conditioner. She also had laceratingly cyan eyes.

I glimpsed them only in passing. She couldn't look me in the eye.

I complimented her on her home. In this case, I wasn't just being gracious, as it really was very attractively furnished, with lots of deep reds and burgundies. She'd been an interior decorator. But for every compliment I gave her, she was apparently intent on giving me 300. She said she'd looked at my Web page after hearing from me, so she'd known I was gorgeous, but now she saw that the photos didn't begin to do me justice. She was sure that mine were the most gorgeous legs she'd ever seen. Nor could she believe how slim I was. 'What do you eat?' she teased, daring a glance at me, 'one meal every other day?' In fact, I said, my boyfriend had recently revealed that before me he'd never had a girlfriend who ate as much. Her face clouded. 'Well, I suppose it's all down to your metabolism,' she said, rather accusingly.

She poured each of us a glass of wine. 'When I was twenty-five,' she sighed, 'I weighed eight stone.' I didn't disbelieve her, but she nonetheless produced a photo album that confirmed that she'd been very much less rotund. Looking at it, I didn't know quite what to say. If I remarked on how gorgeous she'd been, would she hear it as a condemnation of what she'd become? I played it safe and remarked on what incredible hair she'd apparently always had. It didn't please her. 'People always have complimented me on it, yes,' she acknowledged gloomily. It was going to be a very long visit.

She brightened a bit. 'Do you like pizza?' I told her I adored it. 'I'm making some for our lunch,' she said. 'Six years ago, my husband – my *estranged* husband – and I travelled for several weeks in the south of Italy. I was very taken with the pizza that one buys right on the street in Napoli, and determined that I'd learn to re-create it. It's taken me all this time, but I think I've finally mastered it. It's all to do with the stone you cook it on, you see – and of course getting the very best ingredients. And of course the dough. If your dough isn't just right, you could use the best ingredients in the world and it wouldn't be right.'

I hadn't planned on lunch.

She took a long, contemplative sip of her wine and asked, 'Have you always been slim?' Once again I felt as though in a minefield. Would telling her that up until my mid-thirties I was positively skeletal make her resent me? I played it safe and said only that I'd stayed within three or four pounds of the same weight for the past twelve years.

'I do go to the gym, you know,' she said, as though there were a thought balloon above my head that said, I'll bet she never gets off her fat arse.

'Oh, that's marvellous,' I said. 'I keep meaning to start going, but I'm afraid I just haven't the self-discipline for it. I really do admire those who are able to make themselves go.'

'But of course, *you* really have no urgent need,' she said, her resentment becoming more and more palpable, 'not looking the way you do.' She sipped her wine at length again, and I wished fervently I'd stayed home. There's no talking to the unhappily fat. No matter how conciliatory you try to be, how reassuring, you're forever saying the wrong thing.

Tears were racing each other unmolested down her gorgeous huge alabaster cheeks. I pretended not to notice, to be completely enthralled by her furnishings. She sobbed – unignorably – and swiped the tears from her face. 'I worked so hard at making him happy, so very, very hard. And what does he do in the end? What everyone else in my life has always done. He leaves me. For a fucking 24-year-old. A fucking anorexic-looking 24-year-old. Bastard.'

I let a long moment pass. 'I'm really sorry,' I finally said. 'I certainly know too well what it's like being left.'

'For a 24-year-old?' she demanded, making eye contact now, and lots of it. 'For a 24-year-old who looks like she was let out of Belsen eight hours ago?' She got out of her chair and said, 'Come.' I followed her into her study. She touched the keyboard of her PC to bring her screen back to life. I found myself looking at a familiar Website, that of Goddess Danielle, from whom I'd received no response to my email regarding premises. The Goddess was neither particularly attractive nor particularly slender. Indeed, she seemed to have rather a lot to sit on. Nor was she much of a writer. Or speller. 'Well,' Goddess Louise demanded. 'What do you think? Is she gorgeous enough to make a man walk out on the woman who devoted herself to making him happy for pretty close to fourteen years?'

She didn't want an answer. She was busy clicking away on the screen, getting us to a gallery page that depicted Danielle, here looking even hippier than on her portal page, revelling in the obeisance of a little man wearing a nylon stocking over his face. 'Here they are,' Louise snarled, 'in her dungeon. Don't they make a lovely pair?'

She stepped back, apparently expecting that I would want to get a very good look at the screen. I tsk-tsked and shook my head, incredulous at the depravity of the British male.

'As though, for all those years, I didn't bend over backwards to indulge his every erotic whim, however uncomfortable it might have made me.' She grabbed the mouse and clicked the minimise box on the browser window, making her husband and the temptress Danielle disappear. 'I'm sorry,' she said, as though I were insistent on gaping at them, 'but I can't bear looking at them any more.'

We headed back to the lounge. 'I wasn't remotely into kink when I met him, you know,' she said. 'I was a normal woman, a very successful decorator in my own right, who liked things like snogging. Can you imagine? Well, for fourteen years I did neither. The only way it worked for Eric was for me to dominate him. And I did. Without a syllable of complaint. Because I adored him. And I still adore him.' She absolutely exploded into tears. Wary of adding embarrassment to her anguish, I gave it a moment before I went to her. She threw her arms around me and sobbed violently. I stroked her beautiful glossy hair. We rocked together. She finally stopped, and pulled away, ashamed of herself, swiping angrily at her tears.

'I'm sorry,' she said, more accusatorily than contritely. 'You must think me quite mad.'

'I know how much it can hurt to be left,' I said again, wishing I were anywhere else.

'Yes,' she said, tearless now. 'Well.' She took a deep breath. 'Lunch.'

'I hadn't expected that we'd be having lunch together actually,' I said, as though to an American pupil who'd just revealed the loaded gun he'd brought to school. 'I don't want to put you to any trouble.'

She was instantly desperate. 'Oh, but you *must* try the pizza! Six years I've been perfecting it. I can promise you'll never have tasted anything better.' Now she looked extremely fragile. My head was beginning to swim, but I managed a smile.

We went into the kitchen. You could have come in and photographed it at that second for the cover of a women's magazine. Not so much as a spoon was out of place. I can't bear it when people are even tidier than I.

I sat down at the table. She served a little salad containing tangerine sections and sunflower seeds. Absolutely delicious. I told her so. She didn't seem to have heard.

'Since Eric left, I've only had one session,' she said, leaving her own salad untouched. 'And it was a disaster. Halfway through, while I'm beating the guy, I began crying. And I mean, really bawling. He had to ask me to unchain him. He comforted me. A sweet bloke, that one, but now I'm sure I've

The Temple Discotheque in Teresa Basire's back garden revolutionised dancing in the United Kingdom. You may think my coiffure comical, but the last laugh is obviously my own.

The Voyeurs in 1977. I dressed like a schoolboy and sang like an angel. And then, after they had pried my terror-rigidified little fingers off the microphone stand, Eddie and the Hot Rods came on.

My friend Mandy and I held two (or, actually, four) defiant fingers up
to antiquated notions of propriety. And then went home to the
suburbs and had cucumber sarnies for tea.

Given the horrors of my early adolescence, and that it isn't in my nature not to grin broadly when someone points a camera at me, I didn't find it easy to be sultry but somehow managed it – a treat!

Mere moments later, three of the most notable names in British pop history asked if they might pose with me, and I, ever gracious, sighed, 'Yes, I suppose so.'

SUBTERRANEANS
the david bowie fan club

EARLS COURT ARENA

MAIN MAN in association with
MEL BUSH and R.C.A. Records
present

DAVID BOWIE

Saturday, May 12th, 1973
at 8-30 p.m.

ARENA £2·00 Incl. VAT

FOR CONDITIONS OF SALE SEE OVER

BLOCK
EE

ENTRANCE
34

ROW   SEAT

A 16★

TO BE RETAINED

Dear Claire,

Thank you for your drawing and note.

Please forgive the amount of time that has elapsed since I
received them but as you know I am either on the road
performing or in the studio recording singles and albums
and until I sit down with a stack of fan mial every two or
three weeks, I don't realise how much has accumulated.

At the moment I am finishing my new album and in a week you
will hear the new single which I have been preparing for all
of you. It is called Rebel Rebel. I am mad on it. Hope
you are.

I want you to all know and tell your mates that the mail I've
been receiving about performing live again is starting to get
to me. I can't promise a month but I think you lot have
lured me back!

You know it is your letters and cards and applause after each
show which makes me able to carry on and devise new ideas and
schemes to entertain you and make me happy. DON'T EVER STOP.

Love on ya!

Ground control to Major Fulfillment:
Colin and I can do it better than you.
In 2001, as I prepared to release my
own very first CD, Himself would tacitly
decline to return the favour. Rotter.

In my pirate days, I did everything in my power to make The Only Ones gigantic but the chap who built our transmitter preferred Dire Straits. There is no accounting for taste, or for its complete absence.

For me and many others at this rally there is no difference between human and animal rights. Issac Bashevis Singer wrote, 'For animals, every day is Treblinka.' I am dedicated to that ceasing to be the case.

Marlin Dog, to whose memory this book is dedicated and who will live always in my heart.

What's that you say, boy? If you don't speak more distinctly, you'll leave Me no choice but to punish you. Severely.

A pleasing view of the famous gams. When a woman is tired of marabou, she's tired of life.

Chloe

If I told you some of the politicians, film stars, and giants of rugby and cricket and squash who've kissed My famously little steppers, you would almost surely gasp 'Cor blimey'. At least you would if you were a Londoner.

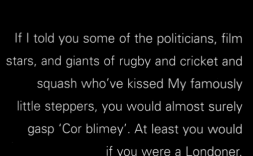

(John Mendelssohn)

Picked my book up in the shop and flipped immediately to the photos didn't you, you ghastly little lurker? And now your palms are as damp as your mouth is dry, aren't they? Can you hear my contemptuous laughter in your mind's ear, worm?

lost him. Nobody's going to go to a mistress who's weak, are they? And he was a regular.'

'Oh, I'm sure he'll be back,' I said. I wasn't sure of any such thing. If she threw another wobbly, I'd leap through a window if that's what it took to get out of there.

The pizza was even better than the salad, and yet eating it was an utterly joyless experience. I told her after the first bite that I just loved it, that I found it sensational, in fact, that it might well have been the best pizza I'd ever tasted. She looked as though I'd accused her of something. 'I got the tomatoes I made the sauce with from a different greengrocer. The original one packed it in and moved to Devon. I'm not convinced that I can count on the new one to the same extent.' My telling her that the sauce was just exquisite regardless of where she'd bought the tomatoes didn't change her expression in the slightest.

She took our plates to the sink. 'I suppose you'd like to see the dungeon now.'

It was next door to the study, and was no dungeon at all. It was a small bedroom painted entirely black, with a couple of hooks on one wall, a few crops and a tawse hanging from a rack on another, and five de Bernardinis lithographs on a third. In the middle of the floor sat a metal chair with handcuffs attached to the legs, and another pair, for wrists, on the seat. In one corner there were an empty dog bowl and a pair of very large high-heeled pumps. I was speechless.

'I know it's not much,' she finally said. 'But my feeling is that it's the woman who makes the dungeon, not the other way round.'

If I'd had a custard pie in hand, she'd have got a faceful of

it. All the way down to Kennington for this! I was too miffed
to speak.

We returned to the lounge. She poured me another glass
of wine. 'I could let you have it for £10 per session,' she
said. I was beginning to get over my disappointment. It was
an improvement, however slight, over my own lounge, wasn't
it? And took only for ever to get down to.

'Of course, if we were flatmates, I wouldn't charge you at
all,' she said. She was back to not being able to look me in
the eye.

'Sorry?'

'Flatmates. Since Eric – I swore I wouldn't think about him
any more today, but there's just no avoiding the subject, is there?
– moved in with Little Miss Perfect Physique, I've been all on
my own. The place is too big for one. Think about it, Chloe.
We could go out and do things together, meet blokes, the lot.'

I probably could have done a better job of keeping the
incredulity off my face. It hurt her.

'You probably think I'd hold you back, don't you?' she
demanded, beginning yet again to cry, but softly this time. 'You
with your gorgeous long legs and slimness. Well, let me tell you
something. There are loads of blokes – and gorgeous ones, mind
you – who quite fancy a larger woman.'

She blew her nose again and regained the ability to look me
in the eye. 'The offer's only good for the next thirty seconds.'

I lied and told her I was flattered. She didn't let me get very
far before she held up her hand to silence me. 'Maybe you'd
better go now,' she said. 'And now I think of it, the dungeon's
all booked up for the next few months.'

On the endless train rides home, it occurred to me that Goddess Louise was the first kinky person I'd ever met who wasn't the very picture of well-adjustedness.

CHAPTER ELEVEN

Diving in at the Deep End

Mistress Jessica, who'd said she might know of premises I could rent, wrote again, providing the mobile number of one Master Stephen, who looked after a well-equipped dungeon up in Wood Green. Away I went.

It wasn't the most salubrious neighbourhood in London, not by a long shot. On the other hand, it wasn't across the Hertfordshire border, and it did lack a washing machine. I liked Master Stephen immediately. He was tiny, with white hair a sixteenth of an inch long growing over a tenth the area it had covered back in the days before it turned white, and a heroic Townshendesque hooter. He couldn't have weighed much more than seven stone, or stood over five foot two. I'd never met a milder-mannered man in my life. It was staggering to imagine that he made his living whipping other men – and even more staggering to imagine that, to whip certain of those other men – those who wanted a woman's touch, but not necessarily a woman – he assumed the guise of Mistress Simone. At least it couldn't have been hard for him to find women's clothing to fit. He'd have had to stuff a pair of socks in my shoes to fill them.

The place belonged to an old mate of Stephen's, a submissive with a fierce fetish for black women. He'd converted his bedroom into a dungeon and moved his bed into the lounge, which looked as though a cyclone had hit it. There were empty beer cans and bottles everywhere, old newspapers, old magazines, most of them depicting dominant black Amazons, and plates with the remains of long-forgotten meals hardened on them. For one such as myself – one who, although gloriously comfortable, will get up off the sofa and make a special trip over if she notices that the rug in front of the TV isn't impeccably flat – merely being in the presence of such chaos was dizzying, but I concentrated on my breathing and got through it.

I met Stephen's housemate and partner in crime, Mistress Fanciful, the tiny, buxom daughter of Malaysian immigrants to New Zealand, a lapsed chef, a young woman of extraordinary shyness. When Stephen introduced us, she kept her eyes on the magazine she'd suddenly started pretending to be engrossed in when I entered. She spent her days hoping that someone who wanted a woman's touch, and who didn't mind women, would ring requesting a session, and sometimes did handsomely.

The deal seemed fair enough by any measure – I would turn over to Stephen 20 per cent of whatever I made in the dungeon, which would be available on a first-come, first-served basis between noon and half past six on weekday afternoons, Stephen's old mate being home, and disinclined to have to wait to use his own toilet evenings and weekends.

I had only one request. 'Do you suppose,' I asked, perfectly deadpan, 'that we might be able to move the whole flat several miles nearer where I live.' When both Stephen and Mistress Fanciful guffawed, I knew I was among kindred spirits.

My first visitor in Wood Green was the posh-accented Cyril, one of those punters who doesn't want to reveal his true interests, but who claims to want just to be ordered about and verbally abused. I would come to learn that only one in ten such guys genuinely does want to be called a pathetic little cockroach by a woman in severe makeup, very high heels, and tight PVC clothing, while the other nine have hidden agendas – and often quite disturbing ones. So it was with this Cyril.

He'd told Me that he'd be bringing something special for Me to wear. It turned out to be a perfectly monstrous green rubber dress that seemed better suited to an abattoir than a dungeon, and looked at least a couple of sizes too big. 'This won't fit Me,' I told him, dropping it back into his arms. 'Far too big, I'm afraid.' It wasn't as though I wasn't already looking My most fetching, or that I wasn't already wearing rubber, albeit black.

He, around thirty, but with a 45-year-old's hairline, and with lips so plump that I suspected collagen injections, nonetheless looked absolutely crestfallen, almost as though about to cry. 'Permission to speak, Mistress?'

'Granted, worm.'

'It really is of the utmost importance, Mistress.'

Some children become attached to a particular blanket, or stuffed animal, or toy soldier. In this poor devil's case, a green rubber dress. Shuddering to imagine the hell his early home life must have been, I sighed and accepted the monstrosity back from him, and went to the bathroom to put it on.

I looked perfectly ridiculous. It swam on Me. It obscured My famous legs from four inches below the knee. The lengths I go to please.

And oh, how I pleased. The poor guy nearly swooned at the sight of Me, licked his obscene fat lips, and reached for himself frantically.

'If you ejaculate, worm, I won't refund a penny of your tribute. It's entirely up to you.'

He managed to let go of himself, although his cock obviously wasn't in favour of the decision. I sat down and made him crawl to Me, thinking that I'd get him to kiss My shoes for five minutes, but he turned out to be very much more assertive than advertised, very much more definite about what he wanted.

He wanted Me to beat him so hard his blood would splatter on the monstrous green dress. And then he wanted Me to castrate him.

Anyone for diving in at the deep end?

'How did you become aware of Me, boy?'

'Your Website, Mistress.'

'And was there anything anywhere on my Website that suggested that I would even consider accommodating either request, boy? Does My Website not in fact make very clear that I don't cater for hard corporal enthusiasts?'

He looked around seven. 'I suppose it does, Mistress, yes. But one can hope.'

He was going to have to be content with what I deigned to give him. I got him up on the cross and whacked him with a cane. 'If it's marking me that Mistress is concerned about,' he said through clenched teeth, 'I can assure Mistress that marks are no problem.'

I gave him a slightly harder one. 'But it isn't that at all, boy. It's that I cater for my slaves' eroticism, not their pathology. And I know very well that one person's pathology is another's eroticism. But I need to feel comfortable in what I'm doing. Is that quite understood, boy?'

'Quite, Mistress.' He was very much enjoying himself.

I had to stop for a minute. It was all getting too much for Me. It was all I could do to maintain My contemptuous tone with him. 'Tell me, boy, what on earth possesses someone like you to ask a Mistress to lop his bollocks off?'

The question discomfited him. My twisting his ear loosened his tongue, though – and stimulated his tear glands. 'I don't deserve balls, Mistress,' he said, a tear skidding down his cheek. 'I don't deserve to be a man.'

I couldn't help but be intrigued. 'Which is the superior sex, worm?' I asked, rhetorically, suddenly enjoying the session very much more.

He didn't hesitate for a heartbeat. 'Women, Mistress.'

I twisted his ear and his nipple simultaneously. What rapturous grimacing! 'And are you not a woefully inadequate creature, one fit only to be ridiculed and degraded by women?'

'Exactly that, Mistress.'

I felt like a solicitor closing in for the kill. 'Then does it not seem only fitting that such a contemptible, inferior creature should be burdened with the anatomical feature that makes it unmistakably a member of the inferior sex?'

You'd never seen anything so cute – it had never occurred to him. He just stood there blinking in confusion while he struggled to get a firm grip on My reasoning. 'Cor,' he finally marvelled, 'you're right!'

And through My quick thinking, a British man retained his manhood on my first day in Wood Green.

My second turned out to be TV day at the dungeon, as no fewer than three crossdressers, only one of whom had given any indication of his proclivities on the phone, came in, one after the other. The first, who called herself nicole, was very nearly as wide as she was tall, but all muscle, and all the muscle, even that on her back, covered with thick black hair. I hoped she wouldn't emerge from the changing room in a strapless evening gown, and she didn't. Rather, she emerged in a brown schoolgirl's frock, crisp white shirt, brown and yellow striped tie, knee-high white socks, and polished black T-bar shoes, licking an oversized lollipop. I experienced a pang of nostalgia for my own school uniform, quickly superseded by the memory of its ghastliness. And I didn't so much as smirk, for which I felt very proud of myself.

It was quite an easy session, if slightly boring, as all nicole wanted to do was cut out paper dolls for half an hour and then get caned a bit before being excused to wank in the changing room. 'Nice little girls don't play with themselves in front of others,' she solemnly recited, pronouncing her l's as w's. And once again I didn't burst out laughing – at least until the poor devil had switched back into the cab driver outfit he'd arrived in and set off home.

After nicole came sue, who must have been six foot six in bare feet, and who made the ceiling nervous in her gigantic stiletto-heeled pumps. If a guy's going to go to the trouble of amassing a femme wardrobe and wax his legs and everything, I wondered, how can he not be bothered to think of a feminine name more exotic than Sue?

She was very nervous, annoyingly so after a while, and not as much fun as she might have been if she'd had a Valium or something on the way over. She wanted Me to read her journal, and to hit her with a paddle every time I discovered a reference to her having tried on her wife's clothing. Judging from the journal, she couldn't have had much time for anything else, and I did a great deal of paddling. Every time I walloped her, sue yelped, 'What I did was very wrong, and I deserve to be punished for it!' in a Yorkshire accent that seemed to become thicker with each blow. Once again Mistress didn't laugh. Sue declined to wank at the end, explaining that the antidepressants she was taking pretty well precluded orgasm.

After sue, the deluge, in the form of jaynette, a gelatinously flabby fifties nostalgist in Marilyn Monroe eye makeup, a tight (indeed, stretched to the verge of ripping) fuchsia angora sweater of the sort Diana Dors might have worn in an injudicious moment, and seamed stockings. Her email had been as full of assurances of her avid heterosexuality as her jumper was of adipose white flesh, but she nonetheless felt called upon, as she staggered from the changing room, to remind Me yet again. As though I gave a toss.

She wanted pretty severe CBT, and no, I'm not going to describe what that involved in this case, not only because it would almost certainly make you squeamish, but also because I dislike thinking about it only slightly less than actually administering it. It's an unpleasant, unseemly business, to be sure, and one I don't think I'm ever going to be entirely comfortable with. And, yes, it does indeed come with the territory. What I will tell you is that by session's end jaynette's tears of joy were ravaging the makeup she'd worked so hard on.

Oh, all right. It means cock and ball torture. But it's rarely as bad as the name would suggest.

I waited for her to change so I could lock up after her, but it turned out that she intended to go back out into the world dressed just as she was, except with her mascara reapplied. 'Be honest, please, Mistress,' she implored. 'Do you think I'm passable?' *Let's just say*, I thought, *that anyone who'd mistake a lime-green Ford Ka for a London Routemaster might indeed think you're a woman, provided it's unseasonably misty, they've dislodged both contact lens, and they took just a quick glance.* 'Absolutely, darling,' I said, 'but I do wonder if you should change into more sensible shoes.'

She beamed from the core of her being and put her arms round Mistress. I had a choice between holding my breath and

passing out from her perfume. She sobbed for a second and let
Me go. 'I can't tell you how happy you've made me, Mistress,'
she said.

All in a dominatrix's day's work, innit?

A day, mind you, that She ended nearly £350 richer than
she began it.

Mr Nic Stoker continued to shower me with compliments and
bottles of champagne. He took me to pricey restaurants and
snarled murderously at waiters who so much as mentioned meat
in my presence. He not only wasn't put off by my having become
a professional dominatrix, but seemed to find the idea terribly
sexy. And when I told him of my fondness for fetish clubs, he
took me shopping at Paradiso in Old Compton Street, where he
bought me a rackful of fetish fashions – and himself a latex
top and trousers to wear to Submission's big tenth anniversary
celebration.

He'd never seen anything like it. I enjoyed his pleasure, but
had to keep nudging him to remind him not to gape, No Gaping
being Rule 2 at this sort of event, right after No Sensible Shoes.
I took him downstairs to the members-only dungeon area, where
a Mistress in a black pageboy wig was enthusiastically flogging
a muscular bloke with a shaved head while a crowd watched
about as interestedly as they would if she'd been a barber in
the City giving a banker a trim. (Rule 3: Look Blasé at All
Times.) He frowned in perplexity and whispered into my ear,
'I can't imagine what he's getting out of it. Look how red the
poor bugger's back is.'

I told him to look at the poor bugger's face. The guy was

obviously transported, rapturous. 'And can't you see his sub-
mitting to her in front of strangers as a gesture of adoration?'

He couldn't, but I had to give him credit for seeming to try.
He deserved a reward.

I had never walked ahead of him, but I did so now,
leading him by the hand into a little alcove. He was grinning
self-consciously, not sure of what was going on, but clearly
excited by the prospects. I reached for his zip and impatiently
undid it. I'd never been aggressive with him before. It was
unmistakably working for him – oh, *was* it! I knelt in front
of him, pulled him to me by the balls, and swallowed him
greedily.

A moment later, I realised we'd already attracted an audience – and one that had thrown Rule 3 out the window – a
semicircle of men vigorously fondling their own pokers in
excitement. I could have tuned them out, but Nic wilted in
embarrassment, and pulled me to my feet, and then to the bar
upstairs.

Cyril, ever more annoyingly grateful for what continued to
dangle between his legs, emailed every day the next week
begging to let him buy me a gift. I chose £1570 worth of shoes
and boots from various on-line purveyors of fetish footwear,
fully expecting him to balk, but he emailed me within two
hours to tell me he'd ordered the lot, and that it would be his
great, great pleasure to take me to dinner at the restaurant of
my choice.

As though I were going to date one of My boys!

My mate The Lovely Sally's birthday was approaching

fast, and I had wanted to take her somewhere very nice, but my finances were in their usual state of disarray, what with the fortune I'd been spending at the vet's, and repairs to my car. The comic possibilities, it occurred to me, were nearly infinite.

I rang TLS. She didn't mind the idea of one of my slaves accompanying us to her birthday dinner, so long as I forbade him to speak and didn't make him spend the meal under the table, which she was pretty sure would embarrass her. I rang Cyril and told him to book a table for three at Manna, an upmarket vegetarian place in Primrose Hill of which I'd read rave reviews. He was audibly thrilled.

He asked if I would be ordering for him. I assured him that I would have it no other way. 'Just like I'm a child?' he asked excitedly, almost certainly unzipping his trousers as he did so.

'Like a helpless little boy who couldn't possibly manage it on his own,' I said, and hung up, leaving him to his own devices.

He lived near Cockfosters, and had collected TLS from Bounds Green en route to Primrose Hill. He'd worn his best suit and had seemingly had more collagen shots injected into his kisser, which was positively bulbous. I laid down the law to him before we were even shown to our table. 'Well behaved little boys are seen, but not heard. Is that quite understood, cyril?'

'Quite, Mistress.'

'You will not address Me as Mistress while we are here, cyril – not that you'll address Me at all. If you *were* to address Me, which, as I say, you won't, it would be as madam. Is that too quite understood?'

'Quite, Mis . . . uh, madam.'

'What a wonderfully well behaved boy you are, cyril!'

He looked as though he might burst out of his suit with pride. He beamed proudly at TLS, who in turn looked at me. And we both burst out laughing.

What a very delicious dinner we had. TLS started with a green papaya salad with chilli and lime dressing, and then, for her main course, greatly enjoyed an organic roast shallot and leek tarte tatin with hasselback roasted potatoes and wild garlic pesto on a bed of leaves. I, who am quite unable to resist aioli, started with filo-rolled asparagus baked with parmesan in a golden pastry and served with aioli, and then was presented, as per my request, with a big bowl of udon noodles and kombu dashi with oyster, enoki, and straw mushrooms, char-grilled bamboo shoots, bok choi, smoky tofu, and julienne vegetables. The wonderfully obedient Cyril, who was expressly forbidden to leave a single morsel uneaten, started with strawberry and rhubarb tiramisu, comprising layers of cassis-soaked sponge fingers, fruit, and creamy mascarpone, and then, for his main course, had both the dark organic chocolate and cognac truffle cake on a raspberry pool and a sundae comprising fresh berries, ice cream, and chunky chocs, all covered with a thick fudge sauce.

A meal to remember!

After several false starts, I finally saw colin, a paediatrician from Milton Keynes, in Wood Green. Every time he'd been on the verge of actually making it down, he had another family health crisis. His father and elder sister had died within a few weeks of one another, and then his mother was diagnosed as having lung cancer and went into a depression that required him not to allow her out of his sight for nearly a month.

His original email had been timid and generic. He'd claimed to be interested in 'all the usual sorts of things', submission in all forms. Then he'd written, 'Something like forced feminisation might prove good fun,' as though we'd been talking about the relative merits of frisbee and badminton on the beach. Eventually I'd managed to ascertain that what he really wanted – what he'd been craving for years, in fact, but had been too repressed to admit to anyone – was to be savagely humiliated.

I've since given a lot of thought to this very common request, and have come to believe that it often stems from a person's unconscious yearning to re-experience as pleasurable what was an especially painful childhood episode. At least half a dozen of my most avid humiliation sluts have described having been weak and timid as adolescents, and shamed by more assertive female classmates. The chromosome that makes these blokes want to re-stage their shaming in an erotic context, and who find it no less thrilling and exhilarating the twenty-fifth time they do so than the first, isn't present in those who want simply never to be reminded of such an incident in any context, erotic or otherwise. Or maybe one group has an extra neural pathway or something. I really do believe that, exactly like homosexuality, it has to do with things over which one has no control whatever. And when society condemns as perverse those who behave erotically as their brain chemistry or genes compel them to without harm to another, you have a situation in which a lot of people are suffering a lot of senseless debilitating pain.

In any event, on the train into town the day I was finally

to meet colin from Milton Keynes, I had an idea. I wouldn't just force him to put on the feminine attire he'd said he'd be bringing along, but would also douse him in Charlie. I popped into the Superdrug just across from the tube and bought a little bottle of it. It cost me nearly a fiver, but if I can't spend a couple of extra quid on my worshippers every now and again, how could I be the supreme dominant goddess of all London?

He turned up exactly on time with a duffel bag full of feminine attire I was to ridicule him for wearing. He turned out to be very much bigger than most of my humiliation sluts, in his early thirties, fit, pleasant-looking without being likely to make any Jude Law fans exclaim, 'God, what could I have been *thinking*!?' He was a few inches taller than I, even in my extremely high-heeled ankle boots, but his extreme nervousness made him seem smaller.

'What have you got in the bag, slut?' I demanded as I accepted his tribute.

He tried to answer, but made no sound.

'Can I guess?' I asked. 'Would it be what you're going to wear for Mistress today?'

He was able to nod.

'Give Mistress a look, slut.' When he was too slow to respond, I grabbed the bag out of his hands, unzipped it, and began describing what I found. 'Some very silky black seamed stockings. And a filmy black baby doll negligee sort of thing. Oh, I suspect you're going to look ever so tarty in *that*. And a black suspender belt with red lace trim. And what have we here, slut? A pair of black patent court shoes with extremely high heels?

Are you going to demonstrate to Mistress how gracefully you can walk in them, slut?'

It looked as though every drop of blood in his body had rushed to his face. He trembled with excitement. I shoved the bag into his arms. 'Change, slut.' I said. 'I'll wait for you in the dungeon. And I expect your makeup to be perfect.'

He took nearly a quarter of an hour to emerge, in a curly blonde wig, shiny black opera gloves, and the things I'd found in his bag. In that way that normal-sized men in drag have, he looked very silly and strangely sexy simultaneously. He'd done a nice job on his makeup. All the blood that had earlier rushed to his face now appeared to have rushed to his cock. 'Turn for me, slut,' I said. 'Slowly. Show Mistress what a sexy little tart you are. Very good. Now walk for Mistress. Pretend you're a runway model.'

He walked very well in his high heels. He'd unmistakably practised a great deal. 'Look at how well the little tart walks!' I marvelled aloud, mockingly. 'Tell me, slut. Is that how you strut around on the street when you're trying to attract customers?'

He gasped with excitement. I laughed at him. 'The shameless little tart loves being ridiculed, doesn't she? Come here, slut.'

He returned to Me. I very slowly ran My hands up his legs from his ankles to the tops of his stockings. 'So wonderfully smooth,' I said. 'Sit down and cross them for Me.'

He seemed dead set on hyperventilating with excitement. He sat and crossed his legs. 'Don't you love the sound of nylon on nylon, little tart?' I mocked him. 'Isn't it just the sexiest sound you know?'

I took out the perfume and beckoned. He stood there with eyes fixed straight ahead while I walked round inspecting him. 'Well, you look very cheap, slut,' I said. 'And your heels certainly make a wonderfully cheap sound when you walk across the tile floor.' I reached inside his baby doll and very gently touched one of his nipples, making him shiver with excitement. 'And you *feel* cheap.' I pulled up the sleeve of his baby doll and licked his shoulder. 'In fact, you even taste cheap, slut. Which leaves only one sense, doesn't it? Do you know which one that is, slut?'

'Smell, Mistress. Olfaction.'

I produced the little bottle of perfume and held it in front of his face. I put My other hand on his chest. His heart was beating around 150 times per minute. I'd guessed right.

'Hold out your wrists, slut,' I said. I sprayed them, gloves and all, with the perfume. I sprayed his neck. And his cock. Generously.

'Do you know, slut,' I whispered, 'that you now absolutely reek of cheapness?'

And then the cataclysm. Letting out the sound of one who'd just walloped his own thumb with a hammer, he ripped off his wig. He sat down and yanked off his pumps, and then his stockings. He couldn't get everything off fast enough, and wailed in frustration. I had no clue what was going on.

'I'm so sorry, Mistress,' he finally managed as he got out of his baby doll and suspender belt and peeled off his gloves. 'So sorry, and so very, very ashamed of myself.'

He dared a glance at me. I spoke to him as a person, rather than as a client. 'Can you tell me what's going on, please?'

He sobbed loudly. 'I always imagined that this would be the most exciting thing in the world, dressing up for a cruel, beautiful woman. And it is. But I can't carry on. I'm too ashamed.'

'You have absolutely no reason to be ashamed, Colin. For a start, a great many boys enjoy playing the little tart for their Mistresses.'

'I was never good at being a little boy,' he said, ignoring my reassurance. 'I didn't fancy any of the things boys were supposed to – sport, and toy lorries, and war games. And I was never aggressive. I was barely out of infant school when other boys, stronger, more aggressive sorts, began bullying me. And letting them felt like the right thing to do, even when they did it in front of girls. I never fought back.'

I told him again that he had no reason to be ashamed. I could think of nothing else.

'My dad was no role model,' he continued, oblivious. 'When my mum said jump, he asked how high. And my older brother was no help, being gay.' He looked at me. This bit was important to him. 'My not being aggressive and traditionally masculine, whatever that means, doesn't mean I'm gay. I've fancied girls from very early on. I don't much like other blokes as friends, let alone as lovers.' It was almost as though I were debating with him.

He looked about to burst into tears. 'I'm so embarrassed. I thought this would be so thrilling and cathartic, and look how it's wound up.'

I ceased in even the smallest way – except for my attire – to be Mistress Chloe, and was instead Claire Mansfield, compassionate and nurturing. I pulled him to me gently and patted the back of his head. 'I can't believe this has happened,' he wailed. 'I am *so* embarrassed!'

'It's all right, Colin,' I cooed. 'Really. I understand.'

He wasn't anywhere near consolability yet. 'But *I* don't!' he wailed. 'My whole life has been leading up to this session. And instead of catharsis, I get . . . *this!*'

He tried halfheartedly to pull away. I didn't let him go. He changed his mind about trying to escape, and squeezed me so hard I felt my eyeballs bulge.

At last, after what seemed five minutes, he finally composed himself again. His makeup, of course, was a disaster. 'I must look a sight,' he speculated accurately. 'You must think me absolutely barking.'

He snatched his feminine attire up off the floor and returned to the loo to change. I felt as though I'd run a marathon with Fiona on my shoulders. I'd never dreamed that being a dominatrix could be such beastly hard work.

He came back into the dungeon in a smart grey suit and brogues. Aside from his red-rimmed eyes, nothing about his appearance suggested the trauma just ended. He spoke to the ground between his feet. 'I appreciate your compassion,' he said. 'And I apologise for having put you through the wringer.'

'You have nothing to be ashamed of, Colin. Nothing at all.'

He nodded gravely and was gone.

That night I received this email from him:

Dear Mistress Chloe:
I don't think I will be seeing you again. While

I realise that my behaviour in your dungeon this
afternoon was probably unlike that to which you are
accustomed, I feel that you could have responded
in a more appropriate manner. Specifically, I think
you should only have got more insulting when I
began to have misgivings about what we were doing.
I believe that the honourable thing would be for
you to refund my 'tribute', as the session was so
deeply unpleasurable for me, but I have no realistic
expectation of your doing so.

Yours regretfully,

Colin.

There's simply no pleasing some people. And sometimes you're
a fool for even trying.

CHAPTER TWELVE

Teapots for Catsuits

You may remember that halfway through the summer of 2001, London nearly suffocated beneath a frightful malodorous cloud that materialised originally over the north-west part of the city and then headed east. Schools and offices were closed. Factories were shut down. The public transport system ceased to function efficiently. (Spot the sarcasm and win a weekend in Majorca!) In televised interviews with Sky TV correspondents with grave expressions, MPs blamed the crisis on one another's parties. The pound weakened against the Euro.

Now it can be told. It was all my fault, and that of a chap in Kew Gardens called Clement, who'd emailed requesting a session – for which he was prepared to pay double my customary rate – that would involve my nearly suffocating him with my smelly feet.

Surmising that he was genuine, I gave him my mobile phone number. I was becoming increasingly aware that submissive men have a remarkable knack for phoning at comically inappropriate moments, and he was no exception. I was examining two new vegetarian pizzas that Tesco had just introduced when he rang. We agreed on a time the following afternoon, and I gave him the address.

I was making it a practice not to go into too much detail in a first telephone conversation, but I couldn't help but wonder why he wanted my feet to smell. He told me that when he was right on the verge of adolescence, he'd been substantially undersized, and his elder sister, very much feeling her own oats, had often delighted in wrestling him to the ground and forcing him to smell her feet, unfragrant from hours of confinement in trainers. Years later, after having repressed his feeling in the interim, he'd been startled and extremely excited to discover, while surfing the Internet, that lots of men were turned on by the same thing. He had since been on a quest to re-create the sublime excitement of those early experiences with his sister, but had been unable to make any of the Mistresses he'd gone to believe that he really wanted their feet to pong. 'You may be assured, boy,' I said, keeping myself from laughing only through a heroic exertion of will, 'that mine will be positively foetid.'

On getting home and refrigerating my newly purchased pizzas, I went through my shoe collection and determined that the pair of ankle boots I'd worn to Submission were the least reminiscent of springtime. I put them on over a pair of tights that I extracted from the dirty clothes basket and passed a pleasant few hours corresponding with prospective visitors to my dungeon. Removing the stockings before retiring, I placed them in a zip-lock plastic bag to prevent their being ventilated. I watched TV for a few minutes and was delighted to learn that it would be sweltering the next day.

I had a better idea than the zip-lock bag, and paid Fiona a rare visit to ask if I could borrow the disreputable-looking trainers she was wearing at that moment, and out of which she'd rarely been glimpsed the previous two years. 'Wassup?' she croaked, clearly delighted with an opportunity to demonstrate how attentively she'd watched the Budweiser advert that very nearly inspired us to break off diplomatic relations with America. I told her I needed her trainers. She looked frightened and confused at the prospect of removing them, but I assured her that I would return them first thing in the morning, and that I would gladly lend her a pair of fuzzy slippers in the interim. She eyed me suspiciously as she slipped them off. I was woozy from the stench. 'You're not going to do anything kinky with them, are you?' she demanded.

Kinky? Your little sister? Oh, Fiona, don't be daft.

I carried the trainers back down to my bedroom at arm's length and with nose averted, and stuffed my stockings deep inside, with a pair of socks that I got out of the basket to keep fresh air from reaching them.

On waking, I immediately put the stockings back on, breathing through my mouth as I did so. The sacrifices I make for my art!

I headed for the tube station. It wasn't sweltering after all. It was hotter than that. My gorgeous little feet felt absolutely soggy in my boots. I had a large area on the platform all to myself. There were a few people in the carriage of the Metropolitan line train I boarded, but they all leapt off at Preston Road to move to others. 'I dunno,' I heard a student say to his mate as they scurried off. 'I think somebody must have died in there last night.'

'Sod that,' his mate said, epitomising the breakdown of morality among British youth. 'A whole bloody army of some-bodies.'

I got to Wood Green several minutes later than I'd hoped to. The streets were strangely deserted. 'Fuck me,' Sir Stephen remarked, sniffing the air as he let me in. 'Did the French invade, or what?' I hurried into the bathroom to change, swapping my jeans and T-shirt for a PVC miniskirt, barely breathing at all, not even through my mouth. When I went into the lounge to say hello to Mistress Fanciful, I found both her and Stephen unconscious.

Clement showed up exactly on time, with the inevitable close-cropped silver hair, but without the rolls of flab that seemed to have become so fashionable among male submissives. He sniffed the air in the hall and beamed with delight. I accepted his tribute and told him to go into the bathroom and strip down while I awaited him in the dungeon.

He was no novice, and knew enough to enter on hands and knees. The stench coming from inside my boots made him no less happy than the smell of sautéeing garlic would make a gourmand. 'Wipe that smile off your face, worm,' I snarled. He shuddered with pleasure and obeyed. He looked at my boots and licked his lips.

'You'd love to be allowed to lick them, wouldn't you, worm?'

'Oh, God, yes, Mistress!'

'Well, I'm not going to let you, not for a long while.' I pulled him over to the St Andrew's cross by his ear, and then to his feet. I strapped him on and then seated myself on the whipping bench opposite. 'Do you know, worm,' I said, 'there seems to be something in My boot.' He was wide-eyed with excitement. 'I think I'm just going to have to take it off.' I took My time unlacing it. Judging from the angle and elevation of his willie, he didn't seem to mind.

Oh, the putridity! And oh, his excitement. Gasping.

'How odd,' I said, turning My boot upside down and shaking it. 'There doesn't seem to be anything in it after all.' I put the boot back on and told him to come and lace it up for Me, which would have been an extremely good trick since he was strapped to the cross. 'I'm not accustomed to being kept waiting, worm,' I said, and he, clever lad, realised that he was to try to twist himself free of his restraints.

When he failed to, I slapped him silly. And then I got in his ear. 'Confess, worm,' I whispered. 'Tell Mistress what a little villain you've been, and what you need to be punished for. If you're a good boy and confess all, there's a chance I'll unlace My other boot too.'

'I've been awful, Mistress,' he blurted eagerly, 'just awful. I've, uh, worked my PA too hard the past couple of weeks. And probably the juniors as well. And I shouldn't even be here with You, Mistress. I'm a married man.'

I pinched his nipple. 'Surely there's much more than that, worm. What else do you need to be punished for?'

He couldn't think of anything, and couldn't think of anything, and couldn't think of anything. I sat back down and began lacing up my boot. Which inspired a moment of transcendent genius.

'I deserve to be punished, Mistress, for wanting to be punished.'

There really wasn't any way I was going to be able not to laugh at *that*, but I managed to make it sound diabolical.

'What a very good boy you are,' I said, ceasing to relace. 'And can you guess how Mistress is going to reward you for being such a good boy?'

He was as excited as I've ever seen a person. The look in his eye was that of a stallion on heat at first sight of a mare.

I unstrapped him, handcuffed his wrists behind him, and got him to lie on his back in front of My chair. As I rested My booted feet on his face, the sounds he made evoked a time millions of years before history.

'I think you have some idea of how bad My feet must smell, don't you, worm? Do you know that I've been wearing these stockings for days now? And you know that it's been very hot and humid, don't you?'

God, to give another human being such joy! It was by far My most pleasurable moment in the dungeon to date. He was actually crying tears of rapture.

I removed My boots with something in excess of the greatest deliberateness possible. The stench! And now he ululated ecstatically as I placed one damp, malodorous little foot and then the other right on his face.

'Open your mouth, worm,' I snapped. I got all five toes of one foot into his mouth, shutting him up, making his writhing even more frantic.

For the next twenty minutes, as I padded all over his face, putting My toes up his nostrils, covering his eyes with the balls of My feet, covering his mouth, his enthusiasm never waned. Finally he pleaded with Me to be allowed to climax. Once he'd done so, it was as though he were a puppet whose strings had abruptly been snipped. He seemed incapable of movement. I told him to remain where he was, and hurried into the bathroom, there to yank off my stockings, to wash my feet in the sink until they were the two freshest in all of Britain, and finally to put on the clean pair of stockings I'd had ready for this moment.

When I returned to the dungeon, Clement was nearly human again. I asked if he'd enjoyed himself. He gave it a long moment's thought. 'It was,' he finally said, 'the best experience of my life.' I decided that My business card wouldn't begin to suffice, and gave him the stockings I'd worn as well. His eyes welled up with tears. 'What a beautiful, generous gesture,' he said, unable to wait even another minute to hold them to his nose.

He left and I went in to give Stephen the house's share of what I'd earned. He asked me how it had gone. 'Best session of my career to date,' I told him. 'Brilliant. If there's a single psychotherapist anywhere in London who sent a patient away today as happy as this bloke, I'd like to meet her.'

I was feeling so good about everything that not even the

prospect of my endless train ride home during the rush hour could dampen my enthusiasm. As I left the dungeon, though, I soon came to the realisation that a large balding bearded man in a rumpled brown suit was following me. I stepped into the pub at the end of the road and ordered a lemonade, I had a look at the *Evening Standard* while I sipped it, and then resumed heading back to the tube station.

And there he was again on the other side of the road. I hadn't carried a can of hairspray to ward off attackers in years. There was a shop I'd noticed before on Alexandra Road, right round the corner from Ravenstone Road, that seemed to be in the business of outfitting streetwalkers. I ducked in and pretended to be in the market for a silver lamé catsuit for a few minutes until I could bear no more of the proprietor's leering.

And there the large balding bearded man was again, in front of the butcher's shop a couple of doors up, leaning against the wall, pretending to be engrossed in the *Sun*. I thought of going into another pub and drinking to my wonderful performance with Clement until the bearded man dropped dead of old age or rush hour ended, whichever came first. But that was entirely too passive for a woman who makes her living reducing arrogant tycoons to whimpering naughty boys. I wound up going over and leaning on the wall right beside him.

'Let's have a look at Page 3,' I suggested. His mouth dropped open. Apparently unable to think of anything cleverer, he actually fumbled for the front of his paper.

'My impression is that you're following me. Why?'

He'd had a minute to compose himself now, and was rather

more impressive – and still not very impressive at all. 'My Mistress told me to, Mistress,' he stammered. 'I was meant to follow you home so I could tell her where you live.'

Ah, a submissive. My heart stopped beating 150 times per minute. Now all I had to do was stop shaking. 'You will not make eye contact with your betters, boy,' I said, wishing I weren't in jeans and a T-shirt for this, wishing I were wearing something in which I felt more intimidating.

He didn't care what I was wearing. He averted his eyes like a good little chap.

'Who is your Mistress, boy?'

The poor sod looked hopelessly perplexed by the moral dilemma I'd created for him. 'I don't think I should say, Mistress.'

He had a little hoop in his left ear. I took hold of it, and used it to turn him towards the window. I pushed his head against it, flattening his nose. What a sight he must have been to the butcher's customers.

'That hurts, Mistress,' he whimpered.

'Who?' I repeated.

'Goddess Louise,' he said, grimacing. One of the butchers was coming out from behind his counter. I hadn't long.

'You will advise the goddess,' I said, 'that where I live isn't hers to know. Is that quite clear, boy?'

'What's all this then?' the butcher demanded.

'Quite clear, Mistress,' the goddess's lackey managed through gritted teeth.

'A very naughty boy preparing to scamper back where he came from with his tail between his legs,' I told the butcher, who seemed to twig immediately. (And why not? We're every-where, you know. We're butchers and animal rights activists, headmasters and labourers, CEOs and dogsbodies, tap dance instructors and barmaids and ballerinas and the guy who sold you your mobile phone. And we're poised to take over.)

'Well, just mind that you don't put his head through me window,' the butcher laughed as he headed back into his shop.

If Goddess Louise had one slave prepared to stalk me, I realised on the train home, she probably had a few. I found the prospect intolerable, and decided, pain in the arse though it was, that I had better find another dungeon.

I went on line and discovered that several new mistresses had been ordained since the last time I'd looked at the listings, and emailed the lot. I was thrilled when one of them, Mistress Wendy, ultra-conveniently located in Wembley, emailed to invite me for a look at her premises. I crossed my fingers, leapt aboard a train, and was there almost before I'd had a chance to marvel adequately at the inappropriateness of the name Mistress Wendy. One wants a professional name that inspires a bit of dread and a bit of lust, doesn't one? For me, Mistress Wendy conjured Peter Pan.

The street she lived on was no less anonymous and suburban than my own. She or her partner, or one of her slaves, was quite the gardener. Herself was in her late thirties, a little bit toothy, but with wonderful blonde hair. What was it about dominatrixing that seemed to make everyone's hair but my own so thick and glossy?

If everyone were greeted as warmly once in a lifetime as her three-year-old Oscar (after Wilde!) greeted me on first meeting, there would be no more wars. He peeked out at me warily from between Mistress Wendy's legs when she opened the door with her two-year-old Alanis (after Morrisette!) in her arms, and then, after sussing that I was someone his mum either liked or might come to like, threw his little arms around my leg and looked up at me with colossal fondness. I was instantly wrapped round his little finger.

It was no great mystery where he got his *joie de vivre* – 'Come in, come in, come in,' she fairly sang as she stepped back to admit me.

Her place was as much a shambles as Goddess Louise's had been a magazine cover, but it soon became apparent why. Oscar was an absolute scirocco of energy, and little Alanis was doing her best to follow in his footsteps. Oscar had great huge sheaves of drawings he thought I ought to see – that very minute! – and his sister was quite the improvisational dancer.

'Well,' I told Wendy, 'these two definitely win the Adorable Children award for September.'

'Oh, but they're a handful,' she said adoringly, barely managing to keep herself from scooping each of them up and embracing them.

She told me about her practice. Her husband – whom, judging from the way her face lit up when she spoke of him, she'd have scooped up and embraced too if he'd been nearby – had only a year before come to feel secure enough in their relationship to confess that he just loved being caned. At first, she'd been horrified. 'But I figured, am I really going to deny the man I adore anything that's in my power to give him?' After a while, she came to revel in his excitement, and actually to look forward to their caning sessions. 'I've always secretly fancied being an actress,' she admitted, 'and it occurred to me that this was as close as I was going to get, playing the role of the cruel headmistress.'

What a charmer she was, witty, solicitous, open, as warm a person as I could remember having met. 'Then it occurred to us that this might be something I could do at home until the children are a bit older.' She'd been a legal secretary before Oscar was born, and it had taken her and her husband a long time to get used to not having her salary. 'Now I'm making half again what I used to, and I don't have to deal with solicitors – except those who come round for a good caning.'

When she laughed, as she did often, her eyes crinkled up in the cutest way. If the premises rental didn't work out, I felt sure I'd want to try to stay in touch with her anyway. Being around her was like the sun coming out.

She put in a tape of *Chicken Run* for the children. 'They've only seen it 4000 times between them,' she laughed, 'but each time they find something new to enjoy.' Sure enough, the two of them were wide-eyed with expectation.

We went down to the basement for a look at the dungeon. It was tiny, but tastefully done and adequately equipped, with a St Andrew's cross, stocks, a whipping post, and, predictably, enough birch canes to stock all the home counties. It was wonderfully tidy, which made me feel right at home. And it had a private entrance. 'I wouldn't have had it any other way,' Wendy said. 'Have Oscar and Alanis see all the naughty men who visit Mummy? I don't think so!' She laughed delightedly. I laughed delightedly. The sun shone more brightly.

'So do you think it might be suitable?' she asked, eyes all a-twinkle.

Given its location, it could have been twice as cramped, half as well equipped, and three times as expensive (she wanted £15 per hour) and I'd still have leapt at the chance to work out of it.

Her mobile phone, which she'd brought down with her, rang, and she was transformed. 'No, not Wendy,' she snarled, her voice no longer light and musical, but half an octave lower, full of disdain, impatience, mocking, bullying. Her face changed along with it. The twinkle disappeared from her eye, the softness from her features. Suddenly I could envisage her in extreme makeup and PVC, and felt a tingling in my loins. '*Mistress* Wendy to you, cockroach. It's £120 per hour, with longer sessions priced *pro rata*, at my sole discretion.

'Yes, there is indeed unrestricted parking. Or if you prefer, Wembley Park tube station is only a seven-minute walk. Tell me, have you visited a professional mistress in the past? I see. And your particular interests?

'As a matter of fact, humiliating cheap little tarts is a particular speciality of mine. No, slut. We are not going to discuss that on the phone. We'll leave that for our first face-to-face meeting, or should I say our first boots-to-face meeting?

'Very well. Off with you then.

'Wanker,' she said brightly, becoming the earlier version of herself in the time it took to break the connection. 'Wanted me to tell him all the things I was going to force him to wear.'

'While he played with himself?' I said.

'So he's phoned you as well!' We both laughed.

We went back upstairs and I met her husband Tony, who'd come home from work early because, as he explained to her, 'I couldn't bear being without you for another minute.' They embraced. 'And that isn't even to mention how much I couldn't bear not seeing a certain little boy and a certain little girl.' Whereupon, as though in an advert, Oscar and Alanis dashed in and greeted their daddy jubilantly, each hugging a leg with all his and her might. And me feeling a perfect gooseberry while they basked at length in their mutual adoration.

I was reminded of a T-shirt I'd nearly bought myself in a little shop in Camden several years before, depicting a panicked-looking woman beneath a thought balloon that said, 'Oh, no – I forgot to have children!'

I looked at the bright side. I had the use of a dungeon very much nearer my home.

The Playboy Channel, whose studio was in the West End, invited me to tape a segment in which I would demonstrate caning techniques. Before the taping, I decided to make a pilgrimage to 10a Dryden Street, where the modern age of British BDSM began with the opening of John Sutcliffe's Atomage.

As a mere slip of a lad, Sutcliffe had dropped RAF bombs on Germany from a Lancaster that he often co-piloted with wee Freddie Laker, who later would pioneer flying people back and forth across the Atlantic in extreme discomfort, but cheaply.

Once home from the war, Sutcliffe went into the family business of restoring fine china and porcelain, mending teapots by day, and by night either dressing up himself or fantasising about beautiful women in gleaming plastic, rubber, and patent leather clothing.

By 1962, he'd got terminally fed up with teapots, and devoted himself to designing and manufacturing kinky clothing for theatre, TV, and film. He called his business Atomage because he thought that there was a sci-fi quality to his gear, and began to prosper after London's most celebrated female impersonator, Danny La Rue, and the producers of the TV series *The Avengers* became clients. It was Sutcliffe who designed the black leather outfit that Honor Blackman wore so notably in the role of Cathy Gale, and it was Sutcliffe who designed the black leather catsuit that Diana Rigg wore even more notably as Emma Peel, almost certainly the No. 1 female object of kinky desire in the English-speaking world in *The Avengers'* heyday.

I will give him all the credit in the world, but not more than he is due. Sutcliffe himself is thought to have been an expediter of the ideas of others, rather than a true visionary. Atomage's famous boot suit, a zip-up catsuit that included both gloves and boots, is thought to have been the bright idea of one of the kinky sorts who found his way to the Atomage workroom in Dryden Street. And it wasn't Sutcliffe, but Ms Edna Franklin, by all accounts a very good sport, who did the really tricky tailoring – and who commonly had to amuse herself at length outside the changing room while an excited customer, trying on his gear for the first time, waited for his hard-on to wilt so he could zip the bugger all the way up.

In 1972, at the urging of his clientele, Sutcliffe began publishing *Atomage* magazine. Horribly designed and amateurish though it may have been, it was successful from the word Go, even though it was essentially just a catalogue depicting models standing there minding their own business. Within five years its readership had begun to clamour so implacably for something a bit juicier that Sutcliffe reluctantly introduced the *Atomage Bondage Supplement*, which actually depicted persons in shiny clothing – *gasp*! – interacting with one another. The BDSM community was transported with delight. 'More, please, Johnny!' it shouted as one. 'More!'

It turned out he shouldn't have listened, as, in 1982, the wife of one of his most avid subscribers was horrified to discover the *Supplement* in hubby's sock drawer, and complained bitterly to the authorities, who dutifully raided 10a Dryden Street in full tactical gear, confiscating everything they could get their hands on. In the years since he'd forsaken teapots for catsuits, Sutcliffe had got pally with a great many of the rich and powerful kinky, but, as if by magic, every last one of them seemed to have gone on holiday when Sutcliffe was formally accused of being a pornographer and put on trial.

Eventually the charges against him were dismissed and all his rich and powerful friends drifted back from holiday, but he was over seventy by that time and understandably burnt out. He quit Dryden Street for Acton Town, nearer his home, ceased publishing the *Bondage Supplement*, and became quite the party animal, showing up at such events as the Swiss Eccentric Fashion Ball and London *Der Putsch* and posing with the mad American BDSM icon Mistress Antoinette (the one from Orange County, California, not my close personal friend from Tampa, Florida). Most of the major figures of European and American kinks were observed to have come to London to kiss his proverbial ring. Dave Roberts, publisher of *Shiny*, acknowledged him as a prime influence. He was knighted. (All right, I made that last bit up, but you get the idea.)

And then, in the autumn of 1986, while putting together what would have been the next issue of *Atomage*, the great man dropped dead. More than a hundred mostly notable persons attended his funeral in Kew Gardens.

Now, fifteen years later, if you asked one of the latex-encased beauties at an event like Submission or Torture Garden or Club Rub if she (or he) has any idea who John Sutcliffe was, the chances are overwhelming that she'd say, 'Who?' – if she can be troubled to respond at all – and 10a Dryden Street is now a launderette.

Standing there looking at it, thinking about the marvellous stories its walls might tell, I resolved to buy 10a Dryden Street on the day my accountant tells me my bank balance has reached nine figures, and to turn it into a shrine.

Murphy's Law states that if you drop a piece of toast, it will invariably land on the buttered side – or, in Australia and New Zealand, the Vegemited side. Mistress Chloe's Law states that if you're all tarted up for a TV taping, you'll invariably encounter someone you know, and who has no inkling as to your secret life. At least this was my experience the morning I taped my *Playboy* Channel segment in full dominatrix drag and severe makeup and then thought that, since I hadn't had a chance meeting on the train with anyone I knew in perhaps nine years, I'd just leave the makeup on to travel over to the dungeon. So who should get on the train at Baker Street but the rigorously down-to-earth Liz Compton, beside whom I'd shouted many a slogan in front of Noble Furs. She glanced at me at first with the perfunctory disinterest with which we Londoners regard one another on buses and trains, and then did a double take, and then finally was delighted to see me, as I was to see her. We agreed that it had probably been close to four years. In the interim, she'd started a dog-walking service and married her longtime partner Eric. They had a fourteen-month old daughter, of whom Lizzy had a photograph. Before I got off the train, she gave me one of her dog-walking business cards and we agreed, in that way of people who expect never to lay eyes on one another again, that we simply had to meet up for a drink at our earliest mutual convenience.

CHAPTER THIRTEEN

What Happens to a Slovenly Little Tart

No sooner had I finally got comfortable at the new dungeon in Wembley, of course, than every woman who'd ever bought a PVC suspender belt at Ann Summers emailed to ask if I'd be interested in renting her facilities. One of these, Goddess Claudia, who was headquartered in Norfolk Square, a short walk from Paddington Station, impressed me with her penchant for very long pauses. Neither full stops nor commas for the Goddess in her emails, you see, but only ellipses with delusions of grandeur. Where the average person is content with three dots, the Goddess often felt that no fewer than a dozen would adequately express her circumspection.

Hi Mistress Chloe:

I am a fellow mistress here in London .... and
noted with interest your need of facilities .... It
so happens that I have some that I would consider
letting to the right person .... or persons ....

Not, mind you, that I envisioned holding her strangely punc-
tuated email against her, not in the face of the fact that
the most grammatically indefensible correspondence I'd ever
received – and don't forget that I've received trunkfuls of
postcards written by musician boyfriends under the influence
of exhaustion, alcohol, cocaine, and extramarital eroticism –
was from an Oxford classics don who wanted to be made to
wear a blue rubber nun's habit and called names.

She had one of those Websites that, with its flickering
torches and animated email icons and text of many, many
colours, resemble a pinball machine. But by far the most
garish thing on it was her kisser. She didn't apply blindingly
red lip gloss liberally only to her lips, but half an inch beyond
them in every direction. I hadn't witnessed such brazen over-
use of cosmetics since, right after moving into my first bedsit and preparing to go out for the evening, I'd looked in
the mirror.

I thanked her for her offer of facilities, but noted that I'd
found some that suited me. She carried on emailing anyway,
never entirely coherently, but ever friendly. I always responded
because I was raised properly.

We finally met a couple of months later at *Bizarre* magazine's big Erotica show at the National Hall, Olympia. She'd

sent me an email saying she was planning to attend ....
and I suggested that we meet there and have a drink together.

I'd been hanging around for an hour when she rang my
mobile to say that she was there too, on the first level at
the Babes-n-Horny booth, where she was apparently buying
butt plugs.

I saw her mouth from half the breadth of the hall away.
The place was full of tarty sexpots hired to attract punters to
the various exhibits, but put together they couldn't have been
wearing as much lip gloss. In boots with sensible heels – sensible
heels! – she came up to my clavicle. She'd have done herself a
favour by devoting some of her lip gloss budget to conditioner
for her wispy, frizzy ginger hair. She had a furtive-looking little
lurker with a pot belly on a leash. We kissed the air beside one
another's faces and beamed. 'Well?' she demanded pointedly
of the little lurker. He dived to the floor and began covering
my own boots, with their extremely not-sensible heels, with
kisses. I stepped away and said, 'Actually, if it's all right, I'd
rather he didn't.'

Goddess Claudia turned out to be South African, and no more
coherent face to face than in email. The extended ellipses really
did suit her. She was forever going out of focus on me – closing
her eyes and smiling beatifically right in the middle of a sentence.
An American would have called her laid back. I realised that she
hadn't kept offering me her premises as a gesture of sisterhood,
but because she was having trouble making the rent on her own.
I wasn't sure what the little lurker was doing under our table. I
wasn't sure I wanted to know.

I was glad when a voice came on the PA to announce that the

National Hall would close in ten minutes – and correspondingly not so glad to discover that the little lurker hadn't driven her, and that she wanted to share a taxi. But something good came of our additional twenty minutes together, as she told me about a fetish club in north London I hadn't heard about, Altocalciphilia. It was apparently on every Sunday night. Unlike at Torture Garden and its ilk, one's boy didn't have to wait in the cloakroom line for forty-five minutes, as it tended to be very much less crowded. We agreed that we would meet up there next Sunday.

It turned out to be held in the basement of a downmarket Brazilian restaurant in Archway. Emil, the boy I'd deigned to allow to drive me, didn't want to leave his new Vauxhall Corsa SXi in such environs. I had him drop me off in front and told him to drive home to Blackfriars and then take the tube back. He didn't seem to realise I was joking, and looked as though he might cry. A slave who doesn't understand his Mistress's sense of humour deserves anything that befalls him.

In the words of Bette Davis, what a dump. It reeked of stale beer. Half the twenty-five or so people there were well into their sixties, and nearly everyone was at least slightly misshapen. They were playing New Order, but at a volume that permitted conversation. New Order works only when played at a volume that makes you worry about the permanence of your fillings. In the play area, a grandmotherly type in horror film mascara and severely jiggly upper arms was beaming toothlessly at the agony of the inadvisedly naked Jethro Tull roadie lookalike she was flogging. It was enough to make one yearn for vanilla. I could certainly understand why Goddess Claudia, who tonight was wearing gallons of pink lip gloss to go with her pink blush and eye shadow, was so delighted to see me.

She reiterated her strong conviction that I really ought to become a partner in her dungeon. I noticed her little lurker waiting in the queue to be mistreated by the jiggly-armed grandmother. I sipped my lemonade with vodka and cursed myself for having let my boy go home. A guy wearing a black leather motorcycle jacket, a suspender belt, stockings, and patent leather court shoes walked past our table for the third time in forty-five seconds. 'Do you mind?' Goddess Claudia asked. I minded, but didn't admit it. She got up and led him by the willie to the play area, where Mrs Jiggles gave her a dirty look but nevertheless surrendered her cat-o'-nine-tails, either deferring to the Goddess's greater beauty or wanting to give her flab a couple of minutes' rest.

An American transvestite with a wonderful immense hooter introduced herself as Kathi, with a K and an i. Being American, she interpreted my smiling and failing to tell her to bugger off as meaning that I longed to become best girlfriends, climbed on to Goddess Claudia's stool, and breathlessly assured me that I was by far the most glamorous person in the place, damning me with faint praise. She turned out not to be a real American, but the Canadian sort. She came from Manitoba and had friends who had friends who had known friends of the singer k.d. lang.

A new couple entered the room and I wasn't so sure that I was the fairest of them all any more. The female half – topless, in a backless PVC skirt, wrists handcuffed behind her, collared and leashed – was an absolute vision. Tall and girlishly slender, graceful even in her extraordinarily high heels, huge eyes appropriately downcast, darkhaired and gorgeously pale, with thick red lips that Goddess Claudia surely would have killed for, she was deferential and vulnerable in a way that made my loins tingle as they hadn't for another woman in years.

Her stocky partner, in a floor-length black leather trenchcoat, might have been fifty, with the inevitable close-cropped steel-coloured hair, a cigar, and a Mussolini-esque swagger. I was reminded of the Joe Jackson classic 'Is She Really Going Out With Him?' which I'd have greatly preferred to New Order at any volume.

They went to the bar. The vision of loveliness looked at the floor while Benito Mussolini puffed his cigar and sized up their fellow revellers.

I asked Kathi with a K and an i if she were submissive. She confirmed it. 'Very well,' I said. 'You will return to continue our conversation in exactly fifteen minutes.' I wished to be alone.

It worked. Benito Mussolini brought his vision of loveliness over two minutes later. 'Me bird,' he said, exuding Lewisham or somewhere nearby, 'has been naughty.' He didn't seem to notice my waving my hand to dispel some of his smoke. He gave her leash a tug but didn't take his eyes off me. 'Haven't you, Nicola?'

The vision of loveliness murmured, 'Yes, Master.' More tingling.

'When I told her she'd be coming topless tonight, do you know what the little tart had the cheek to say? That she didn't want to. Like I bloody care what she wants!'

'Well, that simply won't do, will it?' I said, deciding to play along.

He smiled delightedly and puffed on his cigar. 'Not a bit, it won't.'

That was all I needed. I put my hand on Nicola's sweet little breast, tracing the areola with my fingertip, then lightly flicking the steel ring through her nipple. She gasped. I tingled some more.

I stood. She was around three inches taller than I. My other hand found its way from the small of her back down to her arse. I put my hand under the straps of her skirt. She dared a one-millisecond glance at Me. I gave her nipple ring a little tug. 'I don't recall either I or your Master granting you permission to look at Me, slut,' I snapped.

Benito Mussolini guffawed with pleasure. 'I'm sorry, Mistress,' Nicola murmured. I realised we were wearing the same Superdrug body spray.

'Not nearly as sorry as you're going to be, though,' I said, feeling between her lovely firm cheeks.

'Blimey,' Benito Mussolini exulted. 'You *are* the business, aren't you? Do you fancy whipping her then?'

I took neither my eyes nor my hands off Nicola, whose heart I could feel beating at half again its original rate. I held my forefinger an inch in front of her gorgeous mouth. Her little tongue dutifully emerged to lick it. I can't imagine that my own heart was far behind. 'Not here I don't,' I said, making her tongue chase my finger, taunting her. 'I find it grotty. But in private, very much indeed.'

'But we only just got here,' Mussolini moaned.

I don't know how, but I managed to unhand Nicola, to remount my stool, and to feign great interest in the renewed adventures of Mrs Jiggles and Jethro Tull as I reached once more for my lemonade. If they'd called my bluff, I'd have killed.

They didn't call my bluff. 'Right,' Mussolini sighed, 'then it's back to my place, innit?'

I told Goddess Claudia I was going. She'd apparently seen me with Nicola, and said, 'Good on yer,' whereupon I began liking her a bit more.

Mussolini drove a flash car, of course, a Jaguar XJS that he presumably hadn't fretted about parking in Archway. Nicola, silent, rode in the back. I'd have much preferred to be back there with her, but Mussolini wouldn't hear of my not riding beside him so we could get acquainted. This consisted of his talking about himself nonstop from the moment we pulled away from the kerb until the time we parked in front of his house in St John's Wood.

His name was in fact George. He'd shown great promise as a schoolboy boxer, but had injured his shoulder in a brawl with supporters of a rival football club at seventeen, and so had wound up taking over his dad's plumbing business, in which he'd made a packet. He reckoned that his company must have installed one of every ten power showers in north London, and that he was worth close to £2 million. He was the third or fourth most boring person I'd ever met. The only remotely interesting thing about him was Nicola, and he didn't say a word about her.

His house, with its dark green walls and oxblood leather furniture and paintings of fox hunts, exuded both the most obnoxious kind of masculinity and, in its conspicuous tidiness, someone's neurosis. It was hard to imagine that anyone actually lived there.

As soon as we entered, George pushed Nicola down on all fours and told her to bring us brandy. He went to use the toilet while I tried to ignore his barbaric paintings. It took a while for Nicola to get back to us on her knees with her serving tray. She was visibly upset to notice that George had deposited the butt of his cigar in an ashtray. 'Please, Master,' she said.

'Speak, bitch.'

'Please, Master. May Master's little plaything empty Master's ashtray, Master?'

'Do you suppose I want to live in a pigsty, bitch?' he demanded. 'Do you suppose your Master wants his guests to see his house in disarray?'

She was flushed with shame. It made me start tingling again. 'No, Master,' she said, very softly.

George winked at me and addressed her. 'Into the dungeon on your knees then. We have ways of dealing with slovenly little tarts, haven't we?'

We both followed her into their playroom, three of whose walls were mirrored from floor to ceiling, also mirrored. With the addition of a wide array of women's high heels in men's sizes, a confession box, but not as many tawses, it had everything the dungeon in Wood Green had, including a cage.

'Show us what you do with a slovenly little tart then,' George urged me, lighting a fresh cigar. I didn't very much enjoy his telling me what to do.

I had Nicola remove her skirt, leaving her in only stockings, gloves, shoes, and her collar and leash. I strapped her wrists and ankles to the St Andrew's cross and very slowly drew an invisible line with my fingertip from the bottom of her lovely long white neck to her uppermost pubic hair. She writhed with excitement. Behind me, I heard George unzipping his trousers. Once again I held my fingertip in front of her mouth. Once more her little tongue darted out eagerly to taste it. I reached between her legs and found her clitoris. She gasped. She was as wet as I was.

I flicked at her nipple rings with my tongue. I knelt between her legs and kissed her thighs just above the tops of her stockings while reaching up for her nipple rings. My tongue was in her. She was honey. How could I have foregone this pleasure for so many years?

'Fantastic!' George said, shattering the spell. 'Show her what happens to a slovenly little tart.'

I got up and walked back to him. It was a good thing he had nearly £2 million, a house in St John's Wood, and a Jaguar, because he wasn't going to impress anyone with his tackle. I had a hunch about him, and the brandy had emboldened me to act on it. 'This isn't for you,' I told him. 'You have a choice between buggering off into another room or shutting up.'

His mouth dropped open. What a lot of fillings he had! He caught his breath and started to demand who I thought I was, but I put my hand over his mouth. His own hands got only halfway to my wrists and then receded. Stand up to most bullying little cigar-smokers with fox hunt paintings on their green walls, I've found, and they'll turn to mush in your hand. There was both confusion and exhilaration in his eyes.

I removed my hand. A part of him wanted to defy me,

but a larger part wanted not to. I pulled him to his feet by his ears as he yelped, handcuffed his wrists behind him, and found a wonderful dildo gag for his mouth. I slapped his willie, whose erectness made no secret of how excited he was. I shoved him backwards into the cage, and slammed it shut.

'What happens to slovenly little tarts around here,' I said, 'is that their new Mistress takes them into the bedroom and makes love to them while their arsehole boyfriend or husband or whatever you are devotes some serious thought to being less of an arsehole in future.' When I spat on him, I felt sure he'd ejaculate even without friction.

I unstrapped Nicola, who was looking pretty confused. I was going to have to be decisive. I pulled her face towards mine. My tongue got between her gorgeous huge lips. She moaned and relaxed noticeably. As our tongues intertwined, I took her hands and placed them on my breasts. I felt between her legs. Sopping. I took a handful of her hair and gently pulled her head back from mine, and told her that she belonged to me now. She shuddered with excitement. I turned her round, pulled her ear to my lips, and told her to take me to the bedroom. We ignored George's cage-rattling.

When we reached the bedroom, I told her to put on her favourite CD. She chose Cocteau Twins. We were gentle with one another, though I never allowed her to forget which of us was Mistress. She made me climax with her tongue, I her with my fingers. We didn't stop until several minutes after the Cocteaus had finished their last song. I hadn't made love for so long in centuries. Lying with her afterwards, my chest against her gorgeous slim back, my pelvis against her arse, my legs against hers, was nearly as heavenly as the lovemaking. She said, 'You make me feel safe, Mistress.' I pulled her hair away and kissed the back of her beautiful long neck.

Most of us have had the experience in a supermarket or other public place of seeing a parent being dreadful to his or her child. Usually what keeps me from intervening is the fear that the parent, having been embarrassed, will be doubly awful to the child as soon as I'm out of sight. It occurred to me that Nicola might similarly be in for nasty retribution from her Italian fascist boyfriend once I'd gone.

I confessed my misgivings. For the first time, she spoke to me in the voice she used out in the world. 'That occurred to me as well.' For a moment, I felt slightly embarrassed, as though I'd discovered myself in bed with a stranger.

She turned to face me, no longer slave girl to my Mistress. For the first time, she looked me in the eye. We reached for one another nearly simultaneously and kissed at length. We stared into one another's eyes. 'You're so powerful,' she finally said. 'Help me know what to do.'

'You do submissive really well. Does it come naturally?'

'I used to think so, yeah, but more and more the past several months, I've found myself wondering what it would feel like to be on the other end of the leash. I just don't know that I have the courage, though, and I wouldn't want to hurt him, not for anything.'

'Didn't you see what happened when I defied him, Nicola? He loved it.'

'But I don't know that I have anything like your strength.'

'It's all done with mirrors and smoke. Why don't you bring the brandy in here?'

We each had a large glass. In the dungeon, George rattled his cage impatiently. 'Typical,' I said, pouring her a second glass. 'Most men, when they don't get their way, revert to four years old.'

She laughed. I could tell she was ready. 'Why don't you put something on?' I suggested and she donned a black silk robe in which she looked impossibly delectable. We headed for the dungeon.

I removed George's gag. 'Do you have any idea how bloody long I've been in here?' he demanded, pointedly directing the question at me alone. There was no clock in sight, and the wrist on which he wore his Rolex had been handcuffed behind his back, as it remained.

'No,' I said, 'and neither do you. And you'll speak to Me with the deference I demand from inferior male creatures, or not speak at all. Is that quite clear?' He tried to avert his eyes, but I kept getting back into his sightline. I finally had to grab him by the ears to keep him still. 'Now, how do you address Me, boy?' I asked him.

He looked past Me at Nicola, staring daggers at her. I slapped him. He howled. 'Do I need to repeat the question, boy?'

'You're going to regret this, Nicola,' he said over My shoulder. And got slapped again, harder, for his insolence. I twisted his nipples. He howled again. 'Mistress!' he finally blurted. 'Mistress, Mistress, Mistress!'

'What a clever boy,' I commended him sarcastically. 'And who is in the room with us?'

He was having trouble. I thought grabbing him by the balls might increase the flow of blood to his brain, and I was right. 'Mistress Nicola,' he yelped.

'Exactly right,' I cooed, not letting go his balls, pulling him to his knees by them. 'Kneel before her.'

It was either listen to me or spend the rest of his life as a eunuch. I stepped to the side. Nicola selected a cane off the wall and took My place. 'Things are different now, George,' she said, not entirely convincingly.

He didn't know what to make of this, and looked past her to Me for help. Dive in, I thought. Time stood still. If she didn't take the plunge now, she might never.

She dived, God bless her, backhanding him across the face – hard. 'You will look at Me when I address you,' she said, still a little tentatively, but she was gaining speed. 'No.' She changed her mind. 'You will keep your eyes on the ground.' She stepped behind him and gave him the cane, wincing as he yelped. 'Nicola, for Christ's sake . . .' he began, but then he was yelping again, and again, and again, as she gave him three more. Her eyes were on fire.

'Want more?' she demanded, daring now to step back in front of him.

'Jesus,' he said. Now it was he who was murmuring.

She pushed his head down. He resisted for only a moment. 'My feet,' she said. 'Kiss them. Boy.' I was so proud of her that it was all I could do to keep from hurdling him and carrying her around on my shoulders. 'Yes, Mistress,' he said. It was the sweetest sound I'd heard in weeks. She beckoned. She needed to hold on to me for balance as she stepped on the back of his head with the foot not being worshipped. I took the opportunity to kiss her again.

As I've mentioned, a very large percentage of the email I get from prospective clients appears to be the work of the proverbial roomful of monkeys. Misspellings abound. Punctuation is either nonexistent or seems to have been inserted at random. The syntax resembles that you see in instruction manuals translated from Korean into English by someone with a firm grasp of neither. So, it's a rare treat for me to hear from someone who clearly didn't leave school at six to get a lobotomy.

And an even rarer treat to hear from a new prospect called Antony, who said that he was a top honcho in the London office of an advertising agency with offices in more countries around the globe than it could even keep track of. 'On encountering Your Website last night at the end of a very debilitating day of trying to appease a very important, very stupid client,' he wrote, 'I found myself instantly energised, wholly exhilarated. It wasn't only Your considerable beauty that had this effect, as there are a number of dominant women on the Net whose photos make them out to be ravishing, but the glorious *hauteur* that permeates every word and every image on Your site. Since earliest adolescence, it has always been my most cherished fantasy to be cruelly debased by a beautiful haughty woman. And in You, Mistress Chloe, I believe I may have found exactly the beautiful haughty woman for whom I have been looking so long.'

By the time this beautiful haughty woman got to the end of

that paragraph, she was manifesting very much more delight than *hauteur*. The guy wasn't only literate, but positively poetic!

And then the bad news. He wanted to be shat on. 'I can think of no more profound a debasement,' he wrote, 'than for such a woman to defacate on me, preferably whilst describing me in the most harshly contemptuous terms possible to a fellow dominatrix on the phone.' He would be willing to pay £1000 to have his fantasy brought to life, and offered his mobile number.

The problem was that, outside of the boss of Moskowitz Shoes, I couldn't envisage myself shitting on anyone for £10,000, or £100,000 for that matter, even though I could, to be honest, easily anticipate my inhibitions eroding somewhat with the addition of extra zeroes.

I rang his mobile. He was in his car. As I'd have bet he would, he told me that My voice was a match for My photos. He was delighted by My telling him quite sharply that, if I were interested in his perceptions, I would surely solicit them. Indeed, I'd never heard more delight packed into the three syllables of, 'Yes, Mistress.' I told him I had an appointment available two days hence. He said that he would take it, regardless of how extensively he had to rearrange his schedule.

'You will withhold the additional commentary you wrongly assume Me to be interested in, boy,' I snapped.

I could nearly hear him grinning. 'Of course, Mistress.'

I'd looked at enough dominatrix Websites to know that one was supposed to refer to one's pee as golden nectar or something comparably fatuous, but I'd never seen any such reference for one's faces, and was on my own. 'Whether or not I will choose to void my bowels on you at this session or any subsequent session,' I said, managing neither to perish of embarrassment nor burst out laughing, 'remains to be seen, boy. That's a pleasure you will have to work towards. Only when you've amused Me sufficiently will I even begin to consider it, and I make absolutely no guarantee regarding how long that will take. Is that quite understood, boy?'

'Quite, Mistress.'

He didn't just write gorgeous email, but also knew to show up with a couple of dozen roses, and to present them with eyes appropriately downcast. His clothing looked as though it must have been designed by someone whose surname ended with an i and cost a small fortune. In My black stiletto sandals, I was an inch or two taller than he. His slicked-back hair and ponytail were a nice change from the sea of close-cropped greyness I'd been wallowing in lately. He gave me ten £20 notes. I let four of them flutter to the floor. I told him that until such time as he had demonstrated himself worthy of extraordinary services, I would accept only My ordinary tribute from him. When he knelt down to pick up the money, I stepped on one of his hands. 'Thank You, Mistress,' he said delightedly.

I told him to strip and then crawl into the dungeon. He left his briefs on. I always very much like when they do that, as it gives Me something to start chastising them for the moment they appear. I strapped him to the St Andrew's cross and blindfolded him. 'Tell Me something, boy,' I whispered excoriatingly. 'How is it that you dare to keep your briefs on when Mistress specifically instructed you to strip?'

He didn't answer. I twisted one of his nipples. He yelped in surprise. 'Answer me, boy.'

He didn't answer, and not for the usual reason – that he was too excited to speak. His cock dropped. I realised he was sweating profusely.

'What's my safe word, please?' he asked, a little reproachfully I thought. Ninety seconds into our first session and he wants a safe word.

'How about "advertising"?' I said grasping both his nipples, but actually twisting neither.

'Advertising,' he said.

'Yes. Should you want Me to stop, that's what you'll say.'

'Advertising,' he said again, impatiently – not making sure it was the right word, but invoking it.

'I don't understand,' I said, sounding rather more like Claire Mansfield of Ruislip than the supreme dominant goddess of all London, but too flabbergasted to do better. 'I'm barely touching you.'

'It's frightening,' he said petulantly. 'I don't know if you've ever been in this position, but I can tell you it's not one bit comfortable.'

Every time you think you've got the job sussed, somebody like this comes along.

'Would you be more comfortable if I removed the blindfold?'

He was back to not answering again. 'Yes,' he finally blurted, 'get the bloody blindfold off me! For Christ's sake, don't you know how hard this is, coming in here and letting a complete stranger do these things to me?'

I slipped the blindfold off. 'You came here of your own volition,' I reminded him gently. 'You wanted to be mistreated by a haughty woman, darling. You seemed very excited by the idea. Have I missed something?'

If looks could kill, the one he gave Me would have been fatal. 'Do you know how respected I am?' he demanded. 'Do you know how many other agencies have asked me to head up their creative departments just in the past three months?'

He was getting on my nerves. 'Nine?' I guessed. 'Fourteen? One hundred and twenty-six?'

'Three. Three of the biggest in the UK. So to come in here and be addressed as "boy" is just a bit disorientating. Unstrap me, please.'

I marvelled at how much I'd come to dislike him in so short a time. 'Beg,' I said.

He gave Me another murderous look. 'Beg or stay up there until the next session is scheduled, and I can't remember if anyone else has anyone booked in today.'

'Unstrap me this instant!'

I realised that I'd begun to enjoy myself. I yawned and peeled off one of My gloves, having intuited that a fingernail might require filing. I got an emery board out of My purse and went to work.

'Un-fucking strap me this instant,' he shouted. I shrugged and kept filing.

He laughed, bless his difficult little heart. 'I'm serious,' he said, a lot more civilly. 'Do let me down, will you?'

'Beg.'

He began to fuss and sputter, but realised it would do him

no good. He cleared his throat, swore under his breath, and said, 'Please, Mistress. Will Mistress please unstrap me?'

'More. And don't use first-person personal pronouns. It's unbecoming for one of your extremely low station, boy.' It was exhilarating to think that he'd know what I meant.

'Will Mistress please unstrap . . . Her captive now, Mistress?'

'You are capitalising the H in Her, are you not, boy?'

He laughed again in spite of himself. 'Of course, Mistress. If that's what She demands, Mistress, *She* also being capitalised.'

The tide had unmistakably turned. I put my glove back on and returned to him. 'As a matter of fact, boy,' I said, 'that's precisely what Mistress demands.'

He inhaled sharply. 'Yes, Mistress.'

'These other agencies that have approached you . . . do they realise what a perfectly horrid little pervert you are, boy? Do they realise that all you're good for is being shat on?'

He was in Heaven now, writhing ecstatically, moaning. God, I'm good.

He became a regular. Should you happen to see a copy of *Tied and Teased* or *Serious Mistresses*, you will notice that my advertisements are slicker and more professional-looking than my competitors' by approximately a factor of 1000 to one, the reason being that mine are the handiwork of a top bod at the London branch of an advertising agency with offices in countless countries around the globe.

Within forty-eight hours of my brief appearance on the *Playboy Channel*, I received emails from two blokes who wanted to devote the rest of their lives to me. The first, Jean-Luc, wrote, 'You had an immediate and very strong effect on me. If I may be permitted to say so, I had to unzip my trousers within just a few moments of Mistress first appearing on camera.' He'd found my voice 'literally intoxicating', and had, before the segment was done, resolved to devote the rest of his life to serving me. He proposed to give me access to all his bank accounts, and to leave his job as the assistant chief financial officer of a large international corporation whose name I'd probably recognise to become my live-in sissy maid. He was prepared to provide his own wardrobe. Can you honestly question that such a reaction does a 43-year-old woman's heart good – Jean-Luc's probable resemblance to Jabba the Hut notwithstanding?

The other one, Neil, who didn't write as well, had seen me in *Mayfair*. 'I found you twice as sexy even with your gear on than all those other tarts with their fannies flapping in the breeze put together.' He was a widower, and had been saving up for a Mercedes E320, but had decided he'd rather give me the money. He very much liked the idea of having to pay me for the privilege of being my valet and secretary. His only request was that he be allowed to build a cage beneath my bed and be made to sleep in it naked.

As I believe we've already discussed, I have learned to take such proposals with a grain of salt, and always respond in the same way, by demanding that they send me a bank cheque for £1000 pounds. Thus far, I have received as many such cheques as you have.

Then, hot on the heels of Neil's offer, I heard from alistair, who'd seen my advert in *Serious Mistresses*, and was very keen on trampling – that is, being walked on. He didn't want to grant me access to his bank accounts or otherwise give me money, but would be very pleased indeed to have me exploit his skills as a private investigator. Before his retirement, he'd worked most often for divorce lawyers, he said, but could do pretty much whatever I might require. If I wanted to locate an old acquaintance with whom I'd lost touch, for instance, it would be his great pleasure to find him for me. He hoped that I would deign to stand on his chest in the very high-heeled black sandals I wore in the lower left-hand corner of the advert.

I couldn't immediately think of anyone I wanted to track down, and wrote back curtly to say that if he wanted to book a session, which might certainly include my standing on him, he could ring My mobile just as everyone else did. But then I realised there were indeed some old scores I'd very much enjoy settling, and that I would almost certainly need some help finding the principals.

I was now the supreme dominant goddess of all London. Would Rachel Talbot, the malign Pygmy who'd bullied me so mercilessly during my first few months of grammar school, be able to make a comparable claim? And what of Douglas Hughson, the tennis prodigy who'd had such fun humiliating me; surely *he* deserved a visit from his old neighbour. Nor could I forget Bogweed Bunion, the unabashed sadist who'd made me feel so stupid in his maths class when I hadn't even been able to see the bloody blackboard. I found myself doing something I'd had to train myself not to do – hoping that a submissive man wasn't just talking through his hat.

Alistair didn't seem to be, bless his heart. He replied to

my reply to his original email within ninety minutes, telling me that he was absolutely thrilled to have heard from me, that he regarded me as by far the most beautiful dominant woman in the whole of the UK, and that he was deeply honoured by the opportunity to serve. He would get started the next morning. I lost myself in lurid revenge fantasies, only to realise after half an hour that I was already far too . . . invested in them. Resolving to let sleeping dogs lie, I sent alistair another email, telling him not to bother.

I met Nicola for a drink the following Friday afternoon. She was radiant. She was gaining greater confidence every time she dominated George, and she was dominating him nightly. He seemed to be enjoying their reversal of roles every bit as much as she. The previous evening, she had made him disrobe at the front door on arriving home, and put on the fake fur-trimmed black teddy she'd bought him at a sex shop in Soho that afternoon. He'd been exhilarated, and had confessed, when she deigned to allow him to speak, that he'd had fantasies of forced feminisation since his days as a teenage boxing prodigy. That morning, she had made him wear a pair of her stay-ups under his trousers when he left for work.

He'd been spending a lot of evenings at the office – not really at the office – before we met at Altocalciphilia, but every day that week, he'd come home early, apparently keen to misbehave so Mistress Nicola would have to make him bring her the cane in his teeth. She thought I might have saved their marriage.

That was the good news. The bad was that she didn't feel

right, in view of how splendidly her marriage was doing again, in seeing me carnally, if you will. She'd adored our lovemaking, but George wanted very much to be allowed to watch next time, and she couldn't imagine being comfortable with that, as she could too easily envisage his begging to be included. I could call her old-fashioned if I chose to, but she couldn't bear the thought of him with any woman other than herself.

I'd thought in terms of finding solace in her lovely slender arms during Nic's many, and increasingly extended, sojourns in his Florida office, and was considerably crestfallen. But Mum and Dad didn't raise any weaklings, and my upper lip remained exemplarily stiff, though I hardly heard anything she said for the rest of the forty-five minutes we spent together – except that she quite fancied trying her hand as a professional domina, and wondered if I might be able to recommend someone to put together a Website for her.

The fact was that my own needed a good deal of attention, and I had no good idea of whom to enlist for the job.

CHAPTER FOURTEEN

Alone in the Dungeon with a Psychopath

I am not a natural blonde. I am able to admit this to myself now. I am a natural mousey light brown. Or at least I think I am. I have been colouring my hair for so long that I can barely remember its original shade. And my sister's no help, as she's been dyeing her own since grey first began to sneak into it when she was around thirty-five.

I am not one of those who believe that, if you want your hair done properly, you must find a gay man to do it for you. In the past couple of years, I have entrusted my hair to a pleasant young woman called Claire, as I myself am called by those who do not address me, tremulously, as Mistress. Left to its own devices, my hair frizzes up a treat, displeasing me immoderately. Always I ask Claire to make it lovely and straight. Sometimes it is my whim to have her tease and spray it into an immense globular bouffant evocative of Angie Dickinson in the early days of her being a favourite playmate of Frank Sinatra's Rat Pack. On such occasions, the stalwart Claire will rub her skilful hands together with glee, rather like a supper-club pianist asked to play a song he much enjoys but is rarely asked for, delighted to be able to demonstrate her mastery of a skill too seldom demanded in our hurly-burly, plait-mad modern world.

It was while waiting to be attended by the stalwart Claire one afternoon that I happened to discover in a copy of *The Economist* – some previous client had, perhaps with tongue in cheek, left it among the ancient *Elle*s and *Vogue*s and *Hello!*s – an interesting article about franchising. A Stoke-on-Trent hairdresser called Bartholemew had made a small fortune convincing other Northern hairdressers that they stood to profit by renaming their own shops Bartholemew's, and then by getting yet more hairdressers to pay him to teach them how to open their own salons, likewise called Bartholemew's. By the time I'd finished it, I was so aflame with excitement about the idea of allowing women all over the UK to set up dungeons bearing my imprimatur that I was afraid I might melt the rollers with which Claire would soon fill my hair.

I exaggerate, but I was sufficiently excited about the idea to put adverts in the Ealing *Observer*, *Loot*, the Manchester *Evening Chronicle*, and on the FetishContacts.com Website when I got home, all gorgeous and freshly coiffed, if not excited enough to give it another thought for 72 hours.

Turn a small investment into a career! Mistress Chloe, supreme dominant goddess of all London, invites women 18 and older to learn the art of erotic domination. Work when you choose, and make up to £150/hour. No sexual contact! (Domination is not prostitution.). Email responses only, please. Attach recent photo and be sure to include phone number.

When I checked the new email account I'd set up just for this project, I was flabbergasted to find that I'd received no fewer than 128. There were anorexic-looking seventeen-year-old *au pairs* who seemed to know English only to wave hello to from the opposite platform, and sixty-year-old female bodybuilders with tattoos. There were young BBWs (big, beautiful, that is, fat, women) from Leamington Spa whose extremely soft-focus photographs suggested that they imagined themselves to be trying to line up an audition for *Victoria's Secret*. There were grizzled, pockmarked Glaswegians who had presumably kicked their photographers to a pulp as soon as they had clicked their shutters. I heard from teachers and housewives, waitresses and meter maids, PAs and martial arts instructors and shop girls, loads of shop girls. There were responses that seemed to have been typed by orang-utans, and scrupulously spell-checked ones in which there wasn't a comma out of place. Some of my respondents imagined that the way to my heart was to address me as though I were a submissive, while others were downright plaintive, begging most piteously to be given a chance. Unclear on the concept, obviously.

Of my 128 respondents, approximately three-quarters hadn't

managed to attach a photo, and nearly a third hadn't managed to mention their phone numbers. And we wonder why we no longer have an empire.

I sent emails to the provincial respondents advising them that the first few dungeons would be set up in and around London and assuring them that I'd be in touch as soon as this first phase of the campaign was complete. Then I went to the Marie Celeste – which is what I call the local in which no customer is ever glimpsed, not even (or perhaps least of all) on Wednesday nights, when they offer free salsa lessons – and asked their permission to use one of their upstairs rooms for a little conference of prospective business partners. The manager, an annoyingly shy, apple-cheeked little man of around thirty-five who never once managed eye contact with me, could hardly believe his ears. 'You really want to use one of our rooms? Cor, that's amazing!' He just stood there, shaking his head. I was worried that he might break into tears of gratitude or something.

'So it's a go then?' I asked.

'Oh, I can't say that.' He shook his head furiously. He would have to ring me.

I'd barely walked in my front door when the phone rang. It was the Marie Celeste's actual owner, ringing to apologise for his son-in-law being a cretin, and assuring me that of course I could use their big room upstairs whenever I liked, although he thought a night other than Wednesday would probably be most suitable, as my prospective business partners might find it difficult to hear me over the salsa dancing.

I reread all the emails I'd saved, and made a list of thirteen likely-sounding prospects to phone. I didn't want to doom the whole enterprise with an unlucky number, and so deleted one who hadn't spell-checked before clicking Send, attentiveness to detail being one of the hallmarks of the successful dominatrix.

Not one of them wasn't surprised by the way I sounded on the phone; they all found me very much more pleasant than they'd have expected. Several had imagined that I would have a regional accent. One had been sure that I must be a man conducting an elaborate ruse to meet domineering women. I invited the eight keenest-sounding of the twelve to the Marie Celeste two evenings hence. One was shocked to learn that we would be convening so near to her place of employment.

I toyed with the idea of wearing the PVC minidress and platform ankle boots and officer's cap I often wear to the dungeon, especially since I was hardly more likely to be gaped at in the Marie Celeste than in my own bedroom, but decided in the end on my lavender trouser suit and sensible shoes. It wouldn't do to frighten anyone away.

The one who'd been shocked to find out where we were meeting turned out to be the stalwart Claire, the first to arrive. She screamed with laughter at the sight of me. 'I knew there was something about you,' she said, and resumed shaking her head and chortling. She confided that she was fed up with being a hairdresser. She not only had to pay her salon's owner a daily fee, regardless of how many clients she saw, but also had to hand over 20 per cent of everything she made, exclusive of tips. I asked why, if she had the money to invest in a dungeon, she didn't open her own salon instead. She said that she was fed up with hairstyling. She hadn't enough clients like me, who had her do interesting things. 'It's like making the same two or three meals over and over and over,' she said. It turned out that she'd been a cook in a pub before she became a hairstylist.

I knew that she had an eighteen-month-old daughter, and wondered how her partner felt about the idea of her becoming a professional domina. That took the wind right out of her sails. 'Oh, he doesn't have a clue,' she said, glancing around nervously. 'I can't imagine that he'd begin to understand – old-fashioned Yorkshireman that he is.' I didn't think it would help to mention that many of the kinkiest men I've ever strapped to my St Andrew's cross have been Yorkshiremen. 'Promise you'll never breathe a word to him about it.' I wouldn't have known him if he'd walked into the room and asked me to salsa, so it was an easy promise to make.

Three others showed up almost simultaneously. One of them weighed around 80 pounds, had sunken eyes and a Sinead O'Connor lack-of-coiffure, and looked as though she'd just got out of a concentration camp. Another was as plump as the sunken-eyed one was thin, with spiky hair and an awful lot of mascara. The third was black, with the patently false friendliness of one who worked in a big corporation's Human Resources department.

The five of us bored one another half to tears for ten minutes, talking about the rain and the disgraceful state of the tube, before a rotund ginger-haired young woman with multiple chins burst in, gasping and apologising for being late though it was only two minutes past the hour. Her babysitter had been delayed, and we knew the state of the London Underground. She'd waited nearly twenty minutes for the train to show up in Bromley. The Human Resources one would have loved to have initiated an orgy of small talk on that subject, but I got the impression that no one else was likely to show up, and got started.

I gave them my customary little talk about BDSM as the new homosexuality and about how the only shameful eroticism was that which involves coercion or exploitation. I assured them that, far from hating men, I actually quite like them. I assured them also that it was possible to live a perfectly normal life, including a loving relationship, outside the dungeon. Then I invited each of them to tell what it was about the idea of being a prodomme that most appealed to her. The plump one with the spiky hair, Julie, thought it would be a good way to meet men. The black one, Alexandra – whom we were to feel free to call Sandy – liked the idea of making her own hours. She mentioned also that, as she was very much a people person, she loved the idea of constantly meeting new people. It was getting more surreal by the minute. The stalwart Claire enjoyed the thought of earning as much in an hour as she made over the course of a very busy day as a hairstylist. Jody-from-Bromley, she of the many children and many chins, wanted to take some of the financial pressure off her husband, who was already working in two jobs to support their enormous family, and wasn't trained for anything. And the bulimic or anorexic Gillian, a real piece of work, and make no mistake, believed that her reasons were no one's business but her own.

Her sourness took me aback, and for a long moment I could only gape at her. One of the others cleared her throat. Gillian blurted, 'Because I bloody hate men, all right? Lying bastards! If I could, I'd whip every last bastard one of them until he fainted from the pain.' Whereupon she burst into angry tears. All of which coincided exactly with the apple-cheeked cretin son-in-law of the pub's owner arriving with the drinks we'd ordered. He lost the colour in his cheeks and beat a hasty retreat.

The others looked at one another. Jody-from-Bromley stepped over to Gillian to console her. 'Piss off, will you?' Gillian snarled. It stood to be a very long evening if I didn't get rid of her. I had the idea of getting them all to write down their contact information and a paragraph about their principal misgivings, thinking it would give me an excuse to take Gillian aside and tell her that I didn't think she was a good candidate for professional domination.

We stepped outside. I told her I thought she lacked the temperament to be happy as a domina. There was more pain in her eyes than I may ever have seen in one place. She could barely speak. 'Please,' she finally managed, '*please*. I'm sorry. This could be the lifeline I've been praying for. I've come all the way from Epping. It took me ages. Please. All I ask is another chance.' She began to cry.

I was afraid that if I held her, I might break something. I chanced it. It felt as though I were embracing the skeleton in my biology classroom back at Ealing Grammar. She sobbed alarmingly. I couldn't believe what I'd got myself into.

Back inside, the others had finished their paragraphs and were chattering. One of them said, 'My impression is that she's absolutely barking.' Gillian seemed to have no sense that the comment regarded her. The rest of her being so emaciated and fragile made her eyes appear preternaturally huge, and they were full of unspoken despair. I didn't have the heart to banish her, barking though she was.

Everyone was cooing dutifully at the snapshots of Jody-from-Bromley's children she'd passed round.

We reviewed what they'd written. Alexandra wasn't sure that she'd be able to stick anything up a client's bum. Spiky-haired Julie imagined that she'd feel quite nervous about being alone in a soundproofed dungeon with strange men, for what if one turned out to be a psychopath? Jody-from-Bromley worried that at some point she might encounter one of her clients out in the world, or that her children might find out about her domina alter ego. Claire fretted about being able to lose enough weight so as not to look ridiculous in her kit.

Getting them to think about these things hadn't been a brilliant idea. It hadn't occurred to spiky-haired Julie that she might have to stick anything up anyone's bum, and the more she thought about it, the more uncomfortable she became. She asked if many men wanted this sort of thing. I told her that maybe one in ten craved an enema, or to be made to wear a butt plug during his session. I told her that I too had found the idea prohibitively distasteful at the beginning of my career, but that I'd learned to grin and bear it. I assured her that wearing disposable latex gloves at all times when handling either bums or implements to be stuck up them made one feel very much better about it. I was only making things worse.

'But what about the smell?' she fretted.

'For 120 quid an hour, don't you think you can put up with a bit of pong?' Jody-from-Bromley asked her. 'And what's to keep you from having a can of air freshner close at hand?'

'And it's nothing nurses don't have to do every day, is it?' the stalwart Claire observed bravely.

Julie's discomfort was undiminished, which seemed to amuse the barking Gillian, now smiling for the first time in my sight. Her pleasure was somehow even more discomfiting than her rage.

I tried to divert the discussion to Julie's original concern, about finding herself alone in the dungeon with a psychopath. I told her that neither I nor any other mistress I knew had ever had such a problem. I most assuredly did not mention that I have had exactly the same fear every time I've allowed a strange man into my dungeon. 'And you should keep in mind,' Jody-from-Bromley, whom I was coming to count on more by the minute, suggested, 'that most of the time they'd be handcuffed or strapped down anyway.'

We moved on to the stalwart Claire's concern. I produced the copy of *Tied and Teased* that I'd brought along, and invited them to have a look. 'You'll see that professional dominas come in all shapes and sizes. In fact, several of those I personally find sexiest in this issue are about as far from the Kate Moss ideal of beauty as it's possible to be without starting a new species.' Alexandra, Claire, and Jody converged around the magazine like teenage girls in 1972 around a David Cassidy photo album. Poor Julie, though, apparently had other things on her mind, and Gillian, back to her earlier self, bitterly mumbled, 'If you ask me, Miss Kate Moss could stand to lose a few pounds,' as she got herself a cigarette.

'Have a butcher's at *her*!' the stalwart Claire laughed delightedly. 'She's 12 stone if she's an ounce.'

'But she wears it well, doesn't she?' Jody-from-Bromley marvelled.

'As in the rest of life,' I interjected, 'it's mostly about confidence. You only look as good in your kit as you believe yourself to look.'

Gillian begrudgingly stood up to look over Jody's shoulder at the enormous Mistress Val of Birmingham's full page advert. 'It's obscene for anyone to allow themselves to get that fat,' she sniffed, and sat back down, ignored by all.

'I don't think I can go through with this,' Julie of the spiky hair announced, raining on everyone's parade. 'Not if it involves sticking things up strange men's bums. It just isn't something I could ever feel comfortable with.' She stood up. The goodhearted Jody-from-Bromley and the stalwart Claire made small noises of regret.

'Fair enough,' I said, walking her towards the door. 'I did very much enjoy meeting you, and wish you the best.'

'Good riddance to bad rubbish,' Gillian said under her breath, but not far enough under as to be inaudible.

It turned out that the apple-cheeked cretin son-in-law really was a cretin. He'd apparently been listening to us from behind the door, and hadn't had the sense to scurry off when Julie pronounced herself no longer interested. He was breathless with embarrassment. I could see the portents.

'May I ask what you're doing?' I demanded imperiously.

'Nothing, ma'am!' he gasped.

'Nothing? It certainly appears otherwise. It appears that you've been listening to us through the door.'

He had no answer for that one. Every drop of blood in him had rushed to his cheeks and ears. He glanced furtively at one section of floor after another. I grabbed one of his bright red ears. 'Is that correct, boy?'

'I suppose it is, ma'am.'

He was so pathetic that I couldn't help but laugh out loud. He gulped prodigiously, his enormous Adam's apple enjoying its moment in the spotlight. 'You will address Me as Mistress, boy,' I said.

The little rotter had a hard-on! 'Yes, Mistress!' he blurted dutifully. 'Can I get Mistress and the other mistresses another round, please, Mistress?'

'You may,' I said, and burst into laughter as he scampered eagerly down the stairs. They're everywhere, I tell you, absolutely everywhere.

He was back so quickly and so breathless that I pictured him having run all the way. I was thirsty, but it seemed to me that my prospective protégées might enjoy a little demonstration. 'Come here, boy,' I said after he'd served the drinks. He obeyed. 'On your knees now, hands behind you.' He obeyed, and both the stalwart Claire and Jody-from-Bromley were literally open-mouthed with amazement. 'Submissive men are everywhere,' I said, taking a sip of My lemonade with vodka. 'The more imperious you are, the more you'll see it.' I slowly spilled My drink on the floor. 'Wipe it up, boy.'

He looked around desperately. Not a towel in sight. He did the only thing he could do, removing his shirt. 'What a clever, resourceful boy you are,' I said. 'Isn't he, girls?' They knew enough to give him a little round of applause.

I made him remove and hand over his belt, pushed him on to all fours, and whacked his arse. 'Thank You, Mistress,' he hissed through gritted teeth.

'What a remarkably well-trained boy you are!' I said, meaning it. 'Tell us by whom.'

'By the missus, Mistress,' he said. 'Please, Mistress, another?'

I held the belt out to my prospective protégées. Three guesses as to which of them leapt up to snatch it from me.

'Are you a lying, cheating little bastard?' Gillian demanded, wrapping the buckle end of the belt around her hand for a better grip.

Poor Apple-cheeks. It took him a moment to get to, 'If Mistress says I am.'

'Subhuman filth?'

'If Mistress says so. Yes, Mistress.'

'A disgraceful, worthless piece of shite?' She was purple with rage.

He looked up at me for help. I could hardly blame him. 'Gillian,' I said softly, 'please.'

'Please what?' she raged. 'Please fucking *what*?' She burst into tears and threw the belt at me, missing. 'I come here all the way from Epping to find out about your so-called business opportunity, and all I get is humiliated. Well, you know something? You're all fat, every one of you, and I don't need your bloody business opportunity. You can all sod off.'

Jody-from-Bromley was a saint. Not even this outburst was enough to send her compassion into remission. As Gillian staggered sobbing towards the door, Jody got up and went after her, clearly meaning to console her, only for Gillian to whirl and screech, 'Fuck off!' so loudly that you might have heard her in the downstairs Ladies of the other local, the one where people actually meet up and chat.

Everyone took a deep breath, and then another, followed by a third, and those who hadn't spilled their drinks for demonstration purposes took healthy sips of them.

I picked up Apple-cheeks' belt and invited Alexandra to get in the proverbial driver's seat. 'Do I have to go first?' she wondered, to which I raised an eyebrow, to which she sighed, 'All right then.' She accepted the belt. She looked back at the stalwart Claire. Apple-cheeks, very good boy that he was, remained on hands and knees. Alexandra raised the belt over her shoulder, but couldn't pull the trigger. She laughed nervously, looked back at the stalwart Claire, then cleared her throat and asked Apple-cheeks if he'd been a bad boy. 'Yes, Mistress,' he said. 'Very bad indeed.' She cleared her throat again. 'This is harder than one might suppose, isn't it?' she asked everyone and no one. Another nervous laugh.

'You know,' she finally admitted, 'I can't really think of anything to make him do. Maybe I could have another go later after the others?' She handed the belt back and returned to her seat, draining what remained of her gin and tonic in one swallow.

'Being a good dominatrix,' I sighed, 'is very much about being able to think on your feet, about being imaginative.' I realised that might have sounded more like a rebuke than I'd intended. 'Mistress Claire?'

My hairdresser giggled with embarrassment and came up

to accept the belt, to scowl down at Apple-cheeks. 'So you admit you've been naughty, do you, slave?'

'I do, Mistress. Very naughty, Mistress.'

It was as though poor Claire had kept herself from laughing at every good joke she'd heard over the past decade, and was letting it all out at once. She didn't burst into nervous laughter, but positively exploded. She laughed so hard that she ceased to make a sound, so hard that she trembled, so hard that Alexandra joined in and I had to bite my own lip. Tears streamed down her cheeks. She stamped her feet. 'I can't,' she finally managed. 'I just can't!' I glanced down and saw a smirk trying to establish a toehold on Apple-cheek's face. What a wonderful sport he was!

Claire regained her composure at last, and then immediately lost it again. Laughing too hard to speak, she just waved her hand to convey to me that she too was surrendering her turn.

I was presiding over a disaster.

'I'm getting the impression,' I said, 'that we might be going a little too fast this evening. You will leave us now, boy.' Apple-cheeks began to get up, but I pushed him back down. 'On hands and knees,' I said.

'But what about me?' homely Jody-from-Bromley wondered softly. 'Surely I'm entitled to a go.'

This surprised me. It had been my impression that among Alexandra, the stalwart Claire and her, she was by far the least keen.

'Indeed you are,' I said, and held out the belt to her. She mounted Apple-cheeks like a horse. 'Open,' she snapped, reaching forward to tap his mouth. She stuck the middle of the belt in it, holding both ends in her hands, pulling them back to raise his head. 'Forward,' she said, and he began crawling forward in spite of his considerable encumbrance.

You could have knocked me over with a feather.

'Stop,' she said, and pulled back hard on the belt. She dismounted and walked in front of him. She pushed his head down and slid one of her clog-encased feet beneath his face. 'Kiss, worm,' she commanded. 'I don't want to see a single speck of dust on them when you're finished.' I wasn't the only one who was amazed. Alexandra and the stalwart Claire were gaping at one another. 'And the other,' Jody-from-Bromley – Mistress Judith! – snarled, abruptly withdrawing one foot and replacing it with the other. Then she stepped out of his reach, also abruptly.

She wrapped the belt around his neck and pulled it tight. 'What is your purpose, boy?'

'To obey Mistress,' he gasped. He was erect again.

'And . . . ?'

There was panic in his eyes. 'I . . . I'm not quite sure, Mistress.'

She slapped the top of his head smartly. 'To treat all women with the reverence they deserve, regardless of their age or appearance. Is that not right, boy?' Another slap.

'Absolutely right, Mistress. Totally correct.' He was as good as she, and she was terrific!

She let go the belt, gave me a small smile, and returned to her seat applauded by Alexandra and the stalwart Claire, who added, 'Bravo!'

Having no idea how I was going to follow that – lacking the

presence of mind to try to get them to identify what had made Jody-from-Bromley's performance such a success – I declared the meeting finished and assured them all that I'd be in touch. I gave Apple-cheeks a fiver for his extraordinary service, and one of my business cards, in case he wanted to see me formally in my dungeon.

As I walked home, I tried to figure out how I could keep from hurting the stalwart Claire's feelings so badly that she would consign me for ever to the recalcitrant Fabio. I determined that I would tell her that I had abandoned the idea of franchising, as it indeed appeared I would have to, having found only one in 128 applicants remotely suitable.

I rang Jody at home in Bromley to tell her that I'd been most impressed by her, and in fact regarded her as a born dominatrix.

'That's kind of you,' she said, 'but let me stop you right there.' It turned out that she wasn't interested in a professional career at all, but had come along solely in the hope of learning something she might be able to use in the bedroom with her husband, who in the past couple of months had revealed himself to be both submissive and a crossdresser. I told her I understood and wished her all the best.

On my way to the chemist's the following afternoon, I passed the Marie Celeste. Apple-cheeks ran out and stopped me, most apologetically. He wondered if I might be able to provide Gillian's mobile number.

CHAPTER FIFTEEN

Saving it for the Guv

I got my first celebrity punter in, and not before time. It started with this email:

> Dear Mistress Chloe: I am the assistant to the personal assistant of someone who has seen your Website and is very interested in coming along for a session. But before we can proceed, it is important that you understand that all communication on this subject remains strictly confidential.

Fair enough, I said in my return email.

The next day, I received a follow-up from someone with a different screen name.

Dear Mistress Chloe:
My assistant contacted you on Tuesday regarding
a possible session for the person whose PA I am.
Before we proceed, I would like to confirm your
understanding that this matter will remain absolutely
confidential.

The body of the email I sent back contained a single word:
Confirmed.

A couple of days passed. A few dozen emails from prospective clients without personal assistants came in, and I got my usual dozen or so daily phone enquiries.

Then my second correspondent wrote again.

I apologise for our secretiveness to this point. Were
I to tell you whose PA I am, you would understand
immediately why it is absolutely necessary. Having
now received two assurances that you will under
no circumstances divulge any details of these
communications, or of any interaction that may take
place between you and my employer, I am now
prepared to send you a contract to that effect. Once
you have signed it, had it notarised, and returned it,
we can proceed.

The guy was getting on my nerves in a big way by now. I dashed off this reply:

I am beginning to find our communications tiresome.
It should go without saying that I keep My clients'
identities in strictest confidence. To do otherwise
would effectively end My career as the supreme
dominant goddess of all London. I am too busy to
continue playing cat-and-mouse with you.

He or she wrote back:

My employer appreciates your candour, but is a little
confused about your claim that confidentiality is a
given. Suppose that, offered a great deal of money
by the *News of the World*, for instance, a woman
such as yourself did indeed disclose the identity
of her celebrity clients (not, please understand, that
you are to infer that my employer is a celebrity). It
seems to us that a prospective new client who did
not make a habit of reading the *News of the World* –
and it might interest you to know that my employer
has a multimillion-pound libel suit pending against
a publication very much like the *News of the World*
even as we speak – would have no way of knowing
of her proclivity for treachery.

I found that well-written, and even well-reasoned – and
was sufficiently well-fed-up with the whole affair to delete it
without reply.

They rang me the next day while I was filling my car

with petrol. 'You have known me to this point as 19886, my online screen name,' the guy whispered. 'For purposes of this phone call, you may call me John, though that isn't in fact my real name.'

When I told him I wasn't signing anything, and wished to be done with the whole affair, he blurted, 'Please don't hang up! I had inferred that you were no longer willing to play ball, and –'

'I'm perfectly willing to play ball,' I interrupted. 'On the other hand, I am not about to disclose my real identity to your employer or any other client, and a contract that I sign with anything other than my real name would be quite worthless. Good day.'

'*Please*,' he insisted. 'My employer really does want very much to meet you, and I'm not asking you to do anything I haven't myself done. With what the *News of the World* would probably be willing to pay me for what I could tell them about him, I could probably buy the bloody Millennium Dome.'

I took pity on the guy. 'I'm listening.'

'Proceeding on the assumption that your meeting with him will be in absolute strictest confidence, I would like to schedule an appointment for him to see you in your dungeon this coming Thursday afternoon.' Wendy and her family were on holiday, and I'd booked nothing in yet, so I agreed. 'Splendid,' he said, audibly less agitated. 'We will also need to reserve both the hour before his arrival and the hour after the session. As I'm sure you can understand, he has no wish to be seen by anyone either arriving for or just leaving his own session. Naturally, we are prepared to pay your usual rate for all three hours.'

How could I argue?

When I asked what special requests my unnamed client had, John sighed. 'That's something you'll need to sort out with him personally. He will send you an email describing the fantasies he would like you to bring to life for him at least twenty-four hours before your meeting.'

Raoul – I had decided to give my mystery man a name, and thought a silly foreign one just the ticket – wrote as badly as John wrote well. He was one of that apparently ever-growing number of Britons who believe that plural nouns in most cases are formed not only with the addition of an s, but an apostrophe as well.

Dear mistres Chloe
I am very pleased that my asistant's have finally
sorted our meeting out, I have been looking forward
to meeting you or should I say You ever since I first
saw your website in August I find you very sexy I
trust you understand the need for discretion as I am
very much in the public eye, I am an actor who if
I may say so has done well for himself being in a
number of films that most people have seen. I want
very much to worshipp your beautiful feet, also I
would like for you to control my breathing I will be
bringing something special to wear for You.

Thursday came. I arrived a few minutes past one and tidied up the dungeon, which was already very tidy. The buzzer finally rang nearly half an hour later. I asked through the intercom who it was. A voice said it was whom I'd been expecting. I was tempted to say, 'Oh, right, the film star,' but might well have made myself £375 poorer by doing so.

Mistress Wendy and I stand behind the door when we open it, lest passers-by get an inkling of what goes on in her basement. This didn't go down well with the big steroid abuser who stepped in. 'What's all this then?' he asked gruffly.

When I'm in My kit, I allow no one to intimidate me. 'That depends, boy, on whether you're the one who's now ten minutes late for his two o'clock appointment with Me.'

He snorted dismissively. 'Not bloody likely, is it, love? I'm Himself's bodyguard. Anyone else around at all?'

'No. And you will address Me as madam.'

This guy was too salt-of-the-earth to play along. 'Why don't you save it for the guv, darling?' he said, walking to the end of the hall, ensuring that there were no papparazzi or *News of the World* reporters lurking just round the corner. He knocked on the door to the stairs. 'Anyone in there?'

He stepped outside and waved. Over his shoulder I could see someone in wraparound sunglasses and a hooded sweatshirt being let out of the back of his gleaming black limousine, which was absolutely certain to attract absolutely no attention in this neighbourhood.

He hurried in as though being pursued by rabid autograph-seekers. It was a short dash, but left him breathless.

With his hood and sunglasses, I hadn't a clue who he might be, though I was pretty sure he wasn't Brad Pitt, and virtually positive that he wasn't the late Sir John Gielgud, but he knew very well who I was. 'You're even more dazzling in person than on your Website,' he said, proving once more that, while you might be able to get the boy out of the Lake District, you'll never get the Lake District out of the boy. He might have been fifty.

'If it's your intention to have the session, as scheduled,' I said, 'you will address Me with proper deference, boy. Is that understood?'

He dropped to one knee and bowed his head as though about to be knighted. 'Yes, Mistress. Clearly, Mistress.' Behind him, his bodyguard rolled his eyes.

'And you may dismiss your impudent boy.'

He turned and nodded to the big steroid-abuse-man, who shrugged and headed back outside.

'Your tribute, boy.'

'Sorry?'

'"Sorry, *Mistress*." Your tribute. Present it.'

'Oh, the bread.' Suddenly he'd spent every hour of his life in the East End. 'I don't carry money on me, Mistress. Me office will send it.'

It was my turn to roll my eyes, though, he, with his own averted, wouldn't have seen it. 'Your office, boy, will do no such thing. I don't extend credit.'

He had to ring his bodyguard's mobile to tell him – in the voice of a son of Glasgow's Gorbals – to bring the money in. The bodyguard, when he arrived, seemed pretty disgusted about having been disturbed. 'How much then, guv?' he asked his kneeling charge.

'What was it again, Mistress?' Now he was from the same Italian province as my sometime hairdresser Fabio. 'Five hundred quid?'

I did a quick mental accounting and decided that the annoyance I'd suffered already was worth an additional 125 quid. 'It wasn't,' I said, 'but it is now.'

The bodyguard gave me five crisp bills – the biggest bonanza of my career to date – and buggered off anew.

I told Raoul to kiss My feet. He obeyed very eagerly indeed. 'Bring your gear in your teeth,' I said, 'on your knees.' I headed for the dungeon.

He crawled in, breathless again from his exertion. I told him to put on whatever it was that he had in mind to wear for Me. He removed his shoes and socks and jeans, revealing himself to be wearing a rubber catsuit under his clothes.

I made Myself comfortable in My chair. 'Now the sunglasses and sweatshirt, worm.'

He removed the glasses first, and then pulled the sweatshirt up over his head, hidden no more. 'Now you know,' he said accentlessly, glancing at Me. But the fact was that I knew no more than when he'd been hooded. All I'd been through with his personal assistant and his personal assistant's personal assistant, and I hadn't the vaguest inkling who he was, not the faintest feeling of having seen him somewhere!

He had a hood in the bag, and a pair of very high heels in his own size. The hood had little slits at the eyes, no hole under the nostrils, and a zip across the mouth. Once he had it on, he wanted to be strapped to the St Andrew's cross, and then the mouth unzipped just enough to allow Me to put a narrow rubber tube in his mouth through which he would be able to breathe – provided I allowed him to.

I was careful with him, of course, as I am with all My boys. I pinched the tube often enough to keep him very excited, and released it often enough to prevent brain damage.

'I say,' he said poshly when we were done, and he was pulling his jeans and sweatshirt back on over his rubber second skin (which I began to wonder if he ever removed), 'that was quite marvellous.' I smiled. I saw no reason to remain completely in character. My smile emboldened him, and he suddenly sounded as though he'd never been farther than five miles from Sydney. 'And you know why I was comfortable enough to have such a wonderful time with you, Mistress? Because you treated me like just another chap. You've got no idea how seldom that happens, or how much I enjoy it.'

He really had no idea how easy it had been for me, and on the train home it occurred to me that maybe I should try to get out to the cinema more often.

Nic opened doors for me, and pulled out my chair at expensive restaurants whose waiters he bullied on my behalf, and paid for everything, but never imagine that I didn't reciprocate a treat. For instance, the night we went to dinner with a prospective customer for his software, an Australian networking tycoon, and his date, I didn't run screaming into Greek Street.

The tycoon, Malcolm something, seemed to be trying singlehandedly to refute any claims to refinement his country might have made. He wore pinkie rings on both hands and smoked a cigar, but you could barely smell its smoke over the cologne of which he absolutely reeked. He wore python skin cowboy boots. After kissing my hand in greeting, he held on to it very much longer than either I – or his date – was comfortable with. I wasn't sure if he'd heard my name. He addressed me only as *sweetheart* and *dear*, making both two syllables. As soon as we were shown to our table, he leaned over, put his big fleshy hand on my wrist, and said, 'Whatever you want, sweetheart – the most expensive bottle of champagne they've got on their list, *anything* – you order it. This is all on me.'

Thus began a little testosteronefest, as Nic insisted that the evening was on him. In a minute the debate had been reduced to Malcolm shaking his head and saying, 'Absolutely not. I absolutely will not even consider it,' and Nic sniggering and telling him that he had no choice in the matter. After half a dozen back-and-forths of this sort, Malcolm had a droll idea. 'Well, listen, mate. How about if we get the girls to split it?' He wallopped the table and guffawed, everyone in Soho turned to look at us, and I and his date died of embarrassment.

But the horror was only beginning for her, to whom, while winking at Nick, he said, 'Better go find yourself a good corner to stand on, lovely . . . Nic's looking pretty hungry to me, and his beautiful lady looks like the kind that prefers a really top-drawer champagne.' This time it was Nic's thigh he slapped. Nic, clearly really wanting the guy's business, guffawed, as though at great wit. I would never fully forgive him.

Malcolm lit a cigar. The bloke who'd seated us came over and said, as though it pained him to, that cigar-smoking wasn't permitted in the restaurant. Malcolm stuck the offending item in the corner of his mouth, got his wallet out, and produced a

£100 note. 'My guess, mate,' he said, trying to give the guy the money, 'is that you just changed the rules.'

The guy didn't accept. 'I'm terribly sorry, sir. It isn't in my power to change them.'

Obviously intent on being perceived as a very, very high roller, Malcolm gave Nic a look that asked, Can you believe the cheek of these people, and waved the money impatiently at the guy. 'Then get me 20 Dunhill Silk Cut, OK, sport?' The guy sighed and accepted the £100.

Malcolm immediately began talking to Nick about rugby, and I realised with horror what lay ahead. The men would argue good-naturedly about the most *macho* possible sport while their companions exchanged recipes or gardening tips or something. There was no question but that the evening would be a long one.

Malcolm's date turned out to be his wife, Estelle. She had a 28-year-old's face and a 45-year-old's neck, and was very sweet. She was also more boring than the second, third, and fourth most boring people I'd met put together. Her great passion was her church, St Columb's in Sydney. I learned that there were actually more Catholics than any other kind of Christian in Australia, but that the Anglicans had been slowly reducing their lead the past couple of decades. Of course, she wasn't about to get over-confident, as the Uniting Church, which was very much more aggressive in its recruitment of the country's indigenous people, was coming up fast as well.

She asked which church I belonged to. The mischievous part of me wanted to tell her the Church of the Poison Mind, as in the old Culture Club hit, but the more mature part of me prevailed, and I said that I regarded my relationship with God as a personal matter. I almost wished I'd gone with the Culture Club option, as she flushed in embarrassment – or was that anger? In any event, she regained her composure as quickly as she'd lost it, and told me that she respected my privacy. We would speak no more of religion.

At least for five minutes. After telling me that her facelift (which Malcolm had insisted on) had proved very much more painful than she'd expected, she related that years before she'd been a call girl and a cocaine abuser. Only by accepting Jesus Christ as her personal saviour had she managed to redeem herself. She firmly believed that it was Jesus who'd led her to Mal.

And that, I thought, was a good thing?

If I were ever in Sydney, I had to promise that I would let her take me along to St Columb's. She liked me, but sensed that there was great turmoil in my life – turmoil that would certainly dissipate if I allowed Jesus into my own heart. I sighed and sipped my champagne and sighed again and assured her that I was very happy that Jesus worked for her. 'Oh,' she said, putting her fingertips over her mouth in contrition. 'I did promise that I wouldn't talk about that any more though, didn't I?'

Halfway into our third bottle of champagne, not mentioning the whisky sours with which they'd warmed up for the meal, Nic and Malcolm had reached the point of pretending to slag one another's knowledge of rugby. Nic, getting up, said, 'While I visit the Gents, Mal, maybe you'd like to reconsider that last remark, which I must admit is the most misinformed I've ever heard an English-speaking fan of sport make in my hearing.'

He was grinning broadly. Malcolm howled with mirth, turned to his wife for the first time in days, and demanded, 'Can you believe what comes out of these pommie pooves' mouths, Stella? He fancies that Shaun Edwards is a better halfback than Alfie Langer!'

Finding himself alone at the table with no one to shout at about rugby made Malcolm nervous. He looked round, poured himself more champagne, waved his arms until our server sussed that we needed yet another bottle, and lit himself another cigarette, approximately his 300th since finding out that cigars were forbidden. Then he had an idea. 'Stella, don't you need the Ladies?'

If Malcolm said she needed the Ladies, she apparently needed the Ladies. She got up. If I'd had very much less champagne, I might have had the sense to get up with her, but as it was, I remained, and immediately regretted it. Very afraid that he actually would, but being able to think of nothing better on the spur of the moment, I asked Malcolm to tell me about his business.

He drank half a glass of champagne in one swig and reached for my hand across the table. 'Stella's flying back to Oz tomorrow afternoon,' he said, squinting at me lecherously through the smoke of his cigarette.

I had a pretty good idea of what was coming, but pretended not to. 'Oh, what a pity,' I said. 'I would have so enjoyed getting together with her again.' Come bloody on, Nic. How long does it take to pee?

'I find you attractive, sweetheart. Very attractive. And my guess is that I can do things for you that your little pommie friend can't.' He wanted my fingers, but I kept my hand resolutely balled in a fist, not only to defy him, but also to keep myself from throwing my champagne in his face.

'You've got to have the best legs in the whole of the bloody UK. I've been thinking ever since I saw you and What's-His-Name out in front how much I'd like to have them wrapped round my . . .'

Nic was back, and oblivious. 'So, tell me, Mal, did Claire help you to see the light in my absence?'

In the end, Nic got the account, and a little richer, though, as I saw it, he'd come to owe me in ways about which he had no clue.

CHAPTER SIXTEEN

Who's Rubbish Now?

I had a run of miserable, positively wretched luck. Four punters in a row failed to turn up for their sessions without so much as a syllable of explanation or apology. Then a fifth, who'd seemed to that point to be the keenest would-be slave I'd heard from to date, phoned, just as I was finishing putting on the absurdly lurid makeup for which he'd begged, to admit that he'd lost his nerve.

Through it all, the trampling enthusiast private investigator alistair made it possible for me not to abandon hope. He sent half a dozen emails per day, each more effusive in its praise of my beauty. He wanted desperately to see me, but was severely agoraphobic. When I related that I'd had a string of no-shows, he said he would be only too delighted to track the culprits down for me. He could apparently do so without leaving his PC.

Finally, after countless emails, he summoned the courage to ring my mobile, and proved as pleasingly meek and reverent on the phone as he had on line. He felt that he was about 70 per cent of the way to suppressing his fear of leaving his house long enough to visit my dungeon. When I told him I'd just got a pair of thigh-high boots with very high stiletto heels in which to trample him, he gasped. I don't think I'll ever get so jaded as not to enjoy the sound of a man gasping rapturously at the thought of what I'm going to do to him. In a breath, his agoraphobia was in check. He would be up the next afternoon.

I don't know that I'd ever laid eyes on a less attractive man. He was mostly bald on top, but with little tufts of frizzy ginger curls strewn randomly across the landscape of his otherwise gleaming scalp. His eyes went in slightly different directions, a fact that his extremely thick spectacles only accentuated. He had the narrowest mouth I think I'd ever seen, and tiny grey teeth to fill it. There was something vaguely, but naggingly, hamsterish about his expression, and his attire was very much a match for his face.

And he was just as sweet as could be, scrupulously punctual in spite of the three small anxiety attacks he'd suffered on the train, flawlessly deferential, and obviously thrilled to be near Me. As soon as I let him in, he dropped to his knees, explaining, 'I don't deserve to stand in Mistress's presence.' While he went into the bathroom to strip off, I put on the boots I'd promised.

The poor devil. He had one of the smallest willies I'd ever seen, and I'm a professional dominatrix. I started him off with a few minutes of foot worship and imposed verbal self-flagellation. I'm dependent on the latter for clues as to what epithets to hurl later in the session, when I'm doing all the talking. Alistair's stuff was pretty generic. He was a twisted little perv who deserved to be walked on because he was so contemptible, and spent so much of his day fantasising about being overpowered and mistreated by beautiful women.

I had him lie on his back with his head and torso in the cage. Holding on to the bars, I put one foot on his face, pushing it from side to side, and then made him lick the sole and suck the heel. No matter what I commanded, he whispered, 'Thank you, Goddess,' before complying. What a good boy he was. I put one foot on his chest, got a good grip on the bars of the cage, and then was entirely on top of him. He moaned in pain and rapture, fondling My heels.

'Did I give you permission to touch My boots, insect?' I demanded. His hands flew off them. I bounced on him and he gasped in pain. 'You're a miserable little cockroach,' I snarled down at him, 'fit only to be crushed underfoot, fit only to be stepped on.'

He was absolutely transported, I thought. His tears were tears of joy.

Or were they? Suddenly he was sobbing.

I gingerly returned to *terra firma*. He rolled on to his side and into a foetal position and absolutely convulsed with grief. A nutter.

'Alistair,' I finally said, 'are you quite all right, dear?' My abandoning character seemed only to make things even worse. I slapped him, not as a dominatrix, but as a fellow human being trying to arrest his emotional meltdown. It worked, but only to the extent that he was able to remain at the same level of anguish rather than continuing to spiral downward.

'It's true what you said,' he whimpered. 'Being walked on is all I'm good for. I'm rubbish. Absolute rubbish.' He began to sob again.

'Stop it this instant,' I said. 'I won't hear any more of this. I was only telling you what I understood you to want to hear, darling. You're not to take anything a dominatrix says to you in her dungeon seriously.'

'The truest things are said in jest. I'm an ugly little man, I know that, and I'm reminded of it every day. I can't get a girl to go out with me. I'll probably never be able to. I'm lonely every day of my life, and I'll die lonely as well.'

'But you're not ugly at all,' I lied. I wanted to go on, to tell him that in fact he was most attractive in his own way, but couldn't manage it.

'I am. You should see the looks on the faces of the girls I ask out. Complete incredulity. And I'm not talking about Liz bloody Hurley, mind you. I'm talking about ones that are probably just as lonely as me. And honestly, even if I did manage to lure one out, what would happen if by some miracle I was able to bring her home? I'd be ashamed to be naked in front of her. I mean, just look at me, Mistress – the bit a woman would be most interested in. It's bloody microscopic!' He actually grabbed a couple of clumps of hair, apparently with a mind to yank them free of his scalp.

I pulled his hands away. 'Now just stop it,' I said. 'Have you ever heard that old blues song "It's Not the Meat, It's the

Motion"? Well, it's true. Some of the lovers I've most enjoyed being with have been very much smaller than some of those I had no fun with at all.'

'You're just saying that to make me feel better. Do you think I can't see that? I'm rubbish. All I've ever been is rubbish, and all I'll ever be is rubbish. Rubbish, rubbish, rubbish.'

Now I felt as though I were talking to an eight-year-old. 'Alistair, *stop* it!' I said.

He was wretchedness made flesh. 'All I deserve,' he said, almost inaudibly, 'is to be walked on.'

As you know very well if you've been reading attentively – and did I remember to mention that there's going to be a test at book's end? – this sort of thing happens fairly routinely. A bloke comes to a professional dominatrix with lurid fantasies of degradation. When she begins to bring them to life, the guy panics, and needs to be reassured at length that she thinks of him as an entirely creditable human being. Once this happens, he can relax back into the fantasy.

Except that alistair wasn't getting to that crucial last stage. When, playing my hunch, I said, 'You're quite right, insect. Being walked on is indeed all you deserve,' he twigged what I was doing, but couldn't get back into the proper frame of mind to enjoy it. 'I appreciate it, Mistress,' he said. 'You're very sweet, but the moment's past.'

I gave it one last try. 'The moment will be past, worm, when and if I say it's past.' The look on his unfortunate face told me all I needed to know. I sighed. I felt embarrassed, frustrated, drained. I couldn't remember having felt all three simultaneously in quite the same way.

'Christ,' I sighed. 'Who's rubbish now?'

Aghast, he sat right up and touched my shoulder gently above the glove. Now, in a wink, he was the voice of hope. 'You were absolutely wonderful, Mistress. So beautiful and haughty, and such a gorgeous posh accent. It was I who dropped the ball!'

My bursting into tears surprised me as much as him. I suppose it was the pain I was feeling about Nic's imminent return to Florida finding a crack in my psychic armour or something. Whatever it was, what a pair we made: I, in gleaming black PVC, the dizzyingly glamorous supreme dominant goddess of all London, crying on the hairy shoulder of the United Kingdom's least attractive submissive man. And then my sadness triggered his own, and we were both sobbing.

It lasted only a moment, but what a poignant one. And then came the extremely awkward business of parting. I insisted that alistair take his tribute back. He said that he would do so only on the condition that I allow him another session when he wasn't feeling so vulnerable. I couldn't picture my being able to face him again as Mistress Chloe, but agreed to his condition. I just wanted him to go.

That night, I had an idea. alistair wasn't terribly attractive, and a head case, but extremely sweet, and very clever. I lived downstairs from someone who might as well have been agoraphobic for how often she left her rooms, didn't give a toss about anybody's looks, including her own, would probably cherish the sweetness of another – provided she could put her frightful cynicism aside long enough to notice it – and was very clever. Without alluding to our being sisters, I sent alistair an email asking if he'd be interested in meeting Fiona, pointing out that she would almost certainly rebuff him the first couple of dozen times, but that if he stayed the course, he was apt to wind up in a mutually satisfying friendship. I thought 'relationship' might be putting the cart out of the horse's reach.

Alistair was beside himself with gratitude, though I hadn't actually done anything for him yet. He begged to be allowed to drive me places. I very much fancied the idea of having a chauffeur, but what of his phobia? 'This could be exactly what I need to get over it!' he rhapsodised, and he knew his car would enjoy being driven every now and again, as it had languished in his garage virtually from the moment he'd first driven it home from the showroom.

I eventually agreed to allow him to distribute my promotional postcards. It had cost me 200 quid to get them printed, but then, when push came to shove, I discovered that I hadn't the cheek to dispense them, and they'd been languishing behind my home entertainment cabinet for months. It had been my idea to leave little stacks of them in adult bookstores and fetish boutiques in Soho and Camden, but when I ventured into the bookstores, the managers would invariably leer when they realised I was the blonde-bewigged beauty in the spanking skirt depicted on the front of the card. One – by far the greasiest of the lot, naturally – had even asked if I fancied a drink.

I'd found the fetish boutiques almost invariably staffed by prolifically pierced barely-out-of-teenage numbskulls in bizarre makeup. My asking if I could leave a stack of my cards on their counters invariably cast them into a state of abject confusion and, in several cases, hostility. I found that I didn't enjoy standing there and standing there and standing there while they glared first at one side of the card and then at the other, seeming to imagine that they'd discover the answer to my question among the quotes from delighted past clients. I decided that the whole thing was beneath my dignity before I'd distributed 100 of the 2000 cards I'd had printed.

But alistair was pretty nearly ecstatic when I informed him that I would allow him to pass them out. He drove up and I gave him about half the remaining cards. He emailed that evening – there was no getting through on the phone, as so many prospective punters were calling me, my postcard in hand – to say that he'd distributed them all, and needed a fresh supply. He'd even compiled a detailed list of where he'd left the cards, how many he'd left, and whose authorisation he'd got. It wouldn't have surprised me to learn that he'd got all their national insurance numbers as well.

Delighted with his devotion, I gave him one last chance to retract his request to be my driver. He didn't take it, and the next night when I met up with an old pirate radio acquaintance in Soho, it was he and not some unintelligible cab driver from a country I'd never heard of who drove me home. He insisted that I sit in the back seat, and apologised for the fact that there was no partition between front and back. He wore a suit and a cap that he'd bought specially, and hoped that I would address him as 'boy', as he'd found it terribly sexy when I'd done so in the dungeon. 'It's so Rudyard Kipling,' he observed, and I giggled in spite of myself.

I gathered that his preference was that I treat him as someone

I wouldn't deign to speak to, but the ride home from Soho is a very long one, and my curiosity got the better of me. I asked how he'd realised he was submissive.

'Up until I was seventeen, I was always the smallest kid in my form at school, and it wasn't just the boys who'd bully me, but some of the girls as well. One time I looked over my shoulder as I was running down the hall, and collided with this girl called Sara who was sort of the school slag, and quite fearsome actually. She and her mates picked me up bodily and put me in the rubbish bin. On the one hand, it was bloody awful – it felt like everybody in the whole school was laughing at me – but at the same time, it was fabulous. I spent half that night crying in shame when I thought about it, and the other half wanking.

'I don't know where it comes from. I can tell you that in my family, it was my mum who had all the power. I don't think a day went by that she wouldn't give my dad a very sound scolding right in front of me and my sisters, but he never fought back. You'd think that, having had to witness that sort of thing every day of my childhood, it's the last thing I'd ever want to experience in real life, but I find it quite thrilling, in fact, more arousing than nearly anything. I mean, when I look at *Mayfair* or *Penthouse* or one of those other girlie magazines, it doesn't do a thing for me, but give me one with mean-looking women in black leather, and I can hardly wait to get a hand on myself. And that in spite of the fact that the ones in *Mayfair* and *Penthouse* are generally much better looking.'

He admitted that he was a virgin. In fact, he'd never so much as touched a woman's breast. His sex life to the age of thirty-seven had comprised wanking and visiting Mistresses. He was extremely excited about the idea of my fixing him up with Fiona, even though he wasn't sure he'd be able to perform if the woman weren't awful to him. 'May I please enquire, Mistress, as to whether the woman Mistress has in mind for her obedient boy is in fact mean?'

Well, not really mean, I thought, but bleakly cynical, relentlessly misanthropic. If it's awful you're looking for, mate, you'll have come to the right place.

He drove me two more nights that week, distributed the balance of the postcards, wrote long notes of praise in every guestbook on every fetish Website he could find, and begged for more opportunities to serve. This boy needed rewarding.

I did deep breathing exercises for ten minutes, chanted the mantra, 'I am able to get along with my elder sister for brief periods,' for another five, and headed upstairs. Can you guess what Fiona was doing? 'What do you want?' she coughed, not removing her eyes from the TV.

'Just to chat. We do so rarely any more.'

'That's hardly my fault, though, is it, Claire? You're so bloody hostile I hardly dare say hello.'

'You're right. I apologise. I do have an awful lot on my mind.'

'And I don't?'

Like what, I thought, what programme to stare morosely at next? 'I know you do, Fi. And I did apologise.'

She just glowered at the telly.

'Do you give any thought any more to meeting a bloke, Fi?'

She looked at me again, in disgust. 'And where would I bloody do that, if you don't mind my asking?'

Really good question, I thought. *Maybe a public place of some sort – a pub, or a park, or a bus stop, or the frozen food aisle at Tesco, or some other place where there are apt to be other human beings?* I kept my tongue again. 'Well, I know that for a while you had an advert on Matchmaker UK.'

'Yeah, and all the responses I got were from wankers. Most of them didn't even attach a photo.'

'Was there a photo of you with the ad, Fi?'

'No. I don't have a camera, do I?'

I am able to get along with my sister for brief periods. I am able to get along with my sister for brief periods. I am able . . . 'Don't you remember that I offered you the use of my digital, Fiona?'

'A lot of bloody good that would have done. I don't have the software for downloading from it to my hard drive, do I?'

I am able to get along with my sister for brief periods. 'You can download it from Olympus's Website in five minutes, for Christ's sake. Or you could have downloaded to my computer and put the photos on a floppy to take upstairs.'

'If you came up here to shout at me, Claire, may I ask you to please bugger off back downstairs?'

I am able. I am able. I am able. She is without question the most exasperating, maddening person in human history, but I am able to get along with her for brief periods. I am.

'I'm sorry, Fi. It's just that I get very frustrated. I'd so like to see you be happy, and I thought that . . .'

'What makes you imagine that I'm *unhappy*?' she demanded before going into an extended coughing fit.

Oh, I dunno. Maybe that you spend fourteen hours a day sleeping and the other ten sitting alone in a dark room watching television programmes you're not interested in and trying to give yourself lung cancer or emphysema. I sighed. *I am able.* 'I suppose I'm wrong to make assumptions. It's just that I'd like to do anything in my power to make you even happier.' I don't know how, but I managed that last bit without bursting into laughter. 'I've met someone, a bloke, I think you might fancy. He isn't Pierce Brosnan, but he's very clever, and kind, and reliable. I'd like your permission to give him your email address.'

'Not good-looking, though, eh?'

'Not terribly.' *As though you're La Hurley!*

She shrugged and turned back to *Brookside*.

I sent alistair Fiona's email address and a short note describing her as not terribly glamorous, but clever, and interesting, and very much interested in meeting a bloke. I made no mention of our having sprung from the same womb. I sat back and waited.

CHAPTER SEVENTEEN

Falling off the Face of the Earth

When, in response to my traditional curt, 'Can I help you?' a woman asked if she'd reached the Mistress, I was momentarily disorientated, and found it difficult to get immediately into character.

My first call from a female punter.

How I should talk to prospective punters on the phone had been the subject of an interesting and animated debate between me and my longtime friend Ian, one evening not long before, at the Ship. We'd no sooner sat down with our pints than my mobile rang. It was a submissive man hoping to book a session. Ian was appalled at how cordial and businesslike I was. I explained that in the early going, I'd been corrosively imperious on the phone, but that I'd found it sort of tiring. Then I'd discovered that both Master Stephen and Mistress Fanciful were downright genial with callers, the latter to the point of addressing them as 'darling'. They'd both been much amused to discover that I went to the trouble of getting into character for my initial conversations, and I, duly embarrassed, had immediately taken to being businesslike and polite, even saying 'You're welcome' when punters thanked me before signing off.

Ian thought this woefully ill-advised. A few weeks before, I'd brought the latest issues of *Domination Directory International* to our get-together, and we'd had a good laugh looking at adverts depicting women who'd apparently been encouraged to say 'Cheese!' just as the camera's shutter clicked. We'd agreed that these adverts suggested that the women depicted hadn't a clue about being dominant. 'Which is exactly the impression I'd get,' Ian told me now, 'if you spoke to me as I just heard you speak to that bloke.' I'd thought about it at length and decided that, unless I were in the middle of Safeway, surrounded by fellow bargain-hunters, I would indeed give my callers at least a taste of the bitch they'd encounter in my dungeon.

In any event, my first woman caller, Diane, wanted to bring her husband in as a third anniversary gift. Over the past eighteen months, she'd been tying his wrists to the headboard before climbing atop him, and periodically spanking him, and he'd dropped hints that he'd very much enjoy her watching him being made to suffer at the hands of a professional. They'd bought *DDI*, and had agreed that I was the classiest-looking woman in it. I thought it terribly sweet that she would indulge her husband in such a way, and said I'd be pleased to welcome them to my dungeon at my special couples-celebrating-anniversaries rate, which in fact hadn't existed until that moment.

They turned out to be Jack Sprat and his wife made flesh – in poor Diane's case, a great deal of flesh indeed, and she seemed intent on maintaining every ounce. Before she could shake my hand, she had to switch what looked to be a Cadbury's Flake from her right hand to her left, which in turn involved putting down her bulging Asda bag. She got chocolate on my hand when she shook it.

Her face was set in a perpetual sneer. She wore her lank black hair, which didn't appear to be shampooed terribly often, tucked behind her ears. Husband Douglas, a Mancunian, from the sound of him, a couple of inches shorter and around ten stone lighter, had the pathetic moustache of a schoolboy trying to appear old enough to buy beer, and the smallest teeth I'd ever seen in an adult. He was the very picture of the dominated modern male.

We went into the dungeon. 'Ah,' Diane said, just so that someone would say something. 'So this is where it all happens.' Douglas couldn't have been more nervous to save his life. If, given how he was gnawing away, he had anything resembling a fingernail left by the time we finished, it would be a miracle. I told him to strip down. I put in my Puccini CD. 'Actually,' Diane said with a mouthful of chocolate, 'we've brought something of our own.' It was Fleetwood Mac's *Rumours*, that odious apotheosis of 'soft rock'. I gritted my teeth and kept a stiff upper lip.

I got Douglas up on the St Andrew's cross. He was drenched with either excitement or embarrassment, grimacing expectantly before I'd even picked out a flogger. I gave him a hello-how-are-you whack with the one I chose, and then another. 'I can readily see that you're a very naughty little man, but perhaps you'd like to tell Me specifically about some of the mischief you've been up to lately.'

'He promised before last Christmas that he'd be promoted by now,' Diane said. 'Lying little bugger. Dirty little rotter.'

Not on. One didn't bring the real world into the dungeon like this. And I knew too well what it was like, not getting a very well-deserved promotion, but played along, forcing myself to demand, 'Is that true, worm?'

'I was passed over, Mistress. They gave the job I was hoping for to some hooray with a degree.'

'He's a complete waste of space,' Diane contributed. 'He's been stuck at the same level since three years before we even met. We're never going to get out of Balham.'

I smacked Douglas. He only looked miserable.

'He deserves much harder than *that*,' Diane observed. 'He deserves twice as hard. Me mum told me not to marry him. And me dad as well. I wish to God I'd listened.'

If this is how they wanted to celebrate their anniversary, I reminded myself, it wasn't up to me to judge. I hit Douglas again. Still no trace of rapture. I tried to play along, though. 'You're a terrible disappointment to your wife, little man. How do you feel about that?' I hit him again.

'I used to think he was so clever,' Diane said. 'But he isn't clever at all. He's bloody useless is what he is. He deserves twice as hard as he's getting.'

I mentally composed a short memorandum to myself: No more couples. I switched from the cat-o'-nine-tails to the paddle, which turned a vast expanse of his scrawny arse red. Then I noticed he was crying.

'Hurt the little bastard,' Diane urged me, her mouth apparently full again. 'Make him suffer like I suffer every morning when I wake next to him.'

That did it. I put my paddle down and began to unstrap him.

'What's all this then?' Diane protested. 'I was just beginning to enjoy myself.'

'I'm sorry, Mistress,' Douglas whispered. 'I really do love her, and it hurts so much to think how I've disappointed her.'

'Spineless little apology for a man,' Diane fumed. 'Can't even take what you have coming, can you, Douglas? Well, just wait until I get you home.'

I threw out the rule-book. I whirled to confront her. Just as I'd expected, she was halfway through another chocolate bar. Her mouth was ringed in brown.

'What's *your* problem?' she demanded.

'My problem, you unspeakable bovine monstrosity? My problem is that you have absolutely no conception of how the game is played. It isn't meant to be about cruelty. It's meant to be about love. And the only love I see in here is Douglas's for you.'

She gaped at me, giving me a wonderful view of her

half-melted mouthful of chocolate, but I was only just warming up.

'He didn't get the promotion you wanted him to get? He doesn't bring home enough money to suit you? Well, wonderful news: it's the twenty-first century. You can go out and try your own luck in the working world. Provided you can get through the bloody door.'

I felt bad about that last bit the minute I finished saying it. I had more than enough to criticise without mentioning her eating disorder.

She finally regained her power of speech. 'You can't speak to me like this. Who do you think you bloody are? I'll . . . I'll report you.'

'Please do. Ring the Greater London Better BDSM Board. You'll find them in the directory. Get them to send you a form. And while you're at it, ring *Watchdog* as well.'

'Mistress, please,' Douglas implored me tremulously.

'Get your bloody shoes on,' Diane snapped at him, beginning the arduous task of getting herself back on two feet. 'We're off.'

'Who do you fancy *you* are?' I challenged her. 'Patsy bloody Kensit? You're an obscenely obese eyesore with hair that looks like it hasn't been washed since Guy Fawkes Day. If I were you, I'd count myself very lucky indeed to have any husband, let alone one who loves you enough to suffer for your amusement.'

I gave Douglas my business card and told him he wasn't to hesitate to ring if ever he needed me to defend him against Diane. Hearing this, she suddenly burst into tears, through which she demanded, 'Why does everybody always take *his* side?'

Now it was she who was in agony, seeing which, poor Douglas let out a wail that would have broken Pol Pot's heart and hurried to her, only to be stopped in his tracks by the absolutely murderous look on her face.

'Don't you touch me, you,' she said, 'not after you've turned yet another stranger against me.' Then she burst once more into tears, and was so consumed by anguish that she didn't resist his putting his arms round her, or at least round as much of her as possible. In a moment they were both sobbing for all they were worth. She put her enormous arms round him. He nearly disappeared. They both absolutely howled.

He was the first to be able to speak. 'I love you so very, very much, Di.'

'And you know that I love you too, darling, in my own mad way. Tell me you do!'

'Oh, I do, Di! I do!'

Finally they stopped. And all, miraculously, was forgotten. 'You have no idea,' she told me, blowing her nose into the handkerchief he offered her, 'what a breakthrough this has been for us. It's worth twice what I paid you – three times as much.'

'You're a miracle worker,' Douglas told me. 'I was sceptical when Diane told me we were coming to you, but she was right, as usual.'

'I *am* a monstrosity,' she said. 'No one is more aware of that than me. But sometimes I need to hear it. And I thank you for having the courage to say it. I've been promising for ages that

I'm going to lose weight – ages! Well, now I'm really going to do it.'

I was getting more embarrassed by the moment.

'You don't need to lose an ounce for me to adore you, Di,' Douglas said. 'Not an ounce.' Then they were sobbing in one another's arms again.

I finally got them out, but only after Diane asked for more copies of my business card to hand out at her eating disorders support group. It occurred to me yet again, as I waited for my train home, that there probably wasn't a psychotherapist in all London who got better results than I get.

Two nights later, while I was composing scathing emails to submissive correspondents who hadn't spell-checked with due diligence, Fiona tapped on the door of my lounge, poked her head in, and said she was going out. For the evening. Fiona. I was so giddy with delight that I was just barely able to tell her I hoped she had a smashing time.

There was no sign of her the following day, and the house was eerily tranquil without her agonised coughing. I emailed alistair to find out how everything was going, but received no answer. Wherever they were, they were obviously preoccupied with one another.

When she finally came home early Thursday afternoon, just as I was about to leave for Wembley, she was a changed woman. She was smiling. She was wearing something other than her tracksuit. She'd unmistakably brushed her hair.

All I'd done was save her life.

'Well, howdy, stranger,' I greeted her. 'Long time since we've seen you here at the old homestead.'

Too ecstatic for speech, she just beamed at me. If she'd ever looked so happy in the forty-two years that I'd known her, I couldn't remember it. 'I'm going to go way out on a limb here,' I said, 'and venture a guess that it's going really well between you. Am I reasonably close?'

'It's going fucking brilliantly,' she said, throwing her arms up for the sheer joy of being alive, twirling round. 'I never imagined a man could be so wonderful.'

I am not only able to get on with my sister for brief periods, but to embrace her when I am extremely happy for her, as I was at that moment. It might have been the first time we'd had our arms around each other in two decades, and it reminded me of the great love for her that I usually can't see for the resentment and frustration. 'That's wonderful, Fi, absolutely marvellous. Another romance begun by email then.'

She pulled back and looked at me quizzically. 'What are you on about? I don't even think he has a PC.'

A part of me wanted to leave it, for fear of raining on her parade, but the curious part prevailed. 'pealistair@freeserve.co.uk? That doesn't ring a bell?'

'I told you. He doesn't even have a PC. And who's this alistair when he's at home?'

I felt as though I were back on the yacht trying to make it across the North Sea to the *Ross Revenge*. 'The guy I asked your permission to give your email address to. He's a private investigator – a private eye. Hence pealistair. Are you having me on, Fiona?'

She was reverting to form, getting very impatient. 'I've never heard of any alistair. The man I'm in love with is Dad's boss at Tesco, Roger. You've met him, you mad cow. At Mum's and Dad's. Years ago.' With that she went inside, bounded up the stairs, and apparently got busy smoking and coughing.

I rang alistair. He'd lost his nerve and never even emailed her. What was the point when she was sure to reject him? His voice broke. He blurted, 'I'm sorry, Mistress,' and hung up.

I gave him an hour to ring me back. When he failed to, I rang him again. He wasn't answering. I sent him a text message saying that I had to speak to him. He sent one back saying that he was in no condition to speak to anyone. I sent him another telling him to get on ICQ. I asked who his Mistress was. He didn't know what I meant. I went out on a limb and wrote, 'Whose word is your law, worm?' A couple of minutes must have passed before he finally responded.

'Yours, Mistress.'

'I have come to count on you,' I wrote back. 'You are My property. I allow no one to damage that which belongs to Me. I forbid you even to contemplate hurting yourself in any way.'

This pause was even longer than the previous one. I couldn't just sit there staring at my monitor. I had to get up, and then poke my head outside for fresh air. I felt as though suffocating.

Finally he replied: 'Yes, Mistress.' At that moment, there was no more beautiful phrase in the English language.

Of the preceding six months, Mr Nic Stoker had been in Florida for three. And if absence made his heart grow fonder, there was certainly no telling from his emails, which seemed to grow ever more laconic. I had looked forward to spending Christmas with him. He told me he would be in Florida for Christmas. Well, at least we would welcome the new century together. Wrong again. He'd be in Florida for New Year's Eve as well.

I drove down to Somerset to spend the Joyous Holiday Season with Mum and Dad, and found an Internet café at which to check my email. Nic's communications went from laconic to nonexistent. He rang me on New Year's Eve. Grateful for the few minutes we spent on the phone together, I held my tongue about how his apparent lack of interest in communication was hurting me. And then didn't hear from him for another fortnight.

During this time the needy, insecure part of me seized the reins and composed a hurt and angry email telling him exactly what it thought of his long absences and silences. Days passed, and then more days, and I was in agony. Finally I heard from him.

Dear Claire:
There's nothing about disappointing you that
I like, but the plain fact is that my business
requires me to be away from London for long
stretches, and during those long stretches it isn't
possible for me to write to you in the way that
you obviously require. It isn't fair to either of
us to try to continue at full speed under these
circumstances. Thus, with great regret, I must
withdraw.
    Happy New Year.

For the second time in nine months, I was beside myself. I couldn't eat, but oh, could I drink. I lost a stone. I looked at myself in the mirror and saw Fiona – and didn't give a toss. I was someone men broke up with via email. I was falling off the face of the earth. And didn't realise how good I had had it.

For our first eight years together, Marlin had enjoyed wonderful health. Then, one awful evening, she jumped off my lap as though stung. Following her out of the room, I became alarmed when I saw her staggering like a drunkard, her head over to one side. The vet said she'd suffered the canine equivalent of a stroke. When he kept her in overnight to stabilise her condition, I was ravaged, as I'd never been parted from her before. The following day they wanted to keep her in again, but I knew she would be sad and confused in a strange cage. She was a one-person dog.

Fearing that she might suffer another stroke, the vet prescribed some very expensive drugs that helped get more oxygen to her nervous system. It was a struggle to pay for them – but I'd have paid anything to see her fit and happy. Two years passed serenely until one morning she showed no interest in getting off the bed. When one lives intimately with an animal, one knows immediately when something's wrong, and within thirty minutes I had her at the vets'. They took one look and admitted her for emergency surgery, diagnosing a raging womb infection. I came home alone, biting my fingernails down to the quick while I waited what seemed days for the surgeon's call. Surely I wouldn't lose her like this, not after the struggle we'd endured to get her healthy again after her stroke. The phone finally rang – her womb had been about to rupture, which would surely have killed her had they not been able to remove it in the nick of time. I wept as I drove back to collect her. Once more I insisted on having her at home to recuperate.

People who have never shared their lives with an animal find it hard to understand the sheer joy and unconditional love that such a relationship brings. As I laid her gently on her blanket on the bed, still sleepy and dazed from the anaesthetic, I couldn't have loved my own child more. Marlin Dog and I were as close as two living things ever could be.

Waking the next day, she did something she'd never done before – rolled over to face me, her paws on my chest, her nose inches from my face. We stared at each other for a long time. We would begin every subsequent day together in exactly that way.

Aged ten, she fought her way back to health once more, and we enjoyed four more years together. In her last, we even managed a holiday in Devon, though by then she'd developed cataracts that effectively blinded her, and her back legs had become weak and arthritic. Our daily walks were now only round the block, and very slow. I knew that when her time arrived she'd tell me, as she had told me many secret and wonderful things during our years together. Inevitably, she slowly deteriorated, and I prayed that she would die in her sleep to relieve me of that ultimate responsibility I'd dreaded all her life. But on a bleak Sunday afternoon in early December, she finally told me that she could endure no more. I whispered back that I would do as she asked, and called the vet. In the hour before she arrived, I lay with Marlin and thanked her for all she'd given me.

And she departed the world as peacefully as she'd lived in it.

In my arms.

Adored.

CHAPTER EIGHTEEN

Mistress, You My Woman Now

Seventy-five days after he'd bowed out of our romance by email, Mr Nic Stoker returned to London and rang to ask if I fancied a drink. He saw no reason why we couldn't remain good friends. All the recovery I'd managed to that point went right out of the window, as I found myself wanting very much to run to him.

I'm no nineteen-year-old. Before I replied to his email, I phoned my closest friends to ask what they thought I should do. The Lovely Sally saw no reason that I shouldn't use him to satisfy my sexual needs – she sussed immediately that what he was actually proposing was a shag. The Lovely Debbie suspected that he might have had a change of heart, but hadn't had the nerve to come right out and ask me to come back to him. The Lovely Angie in Brockley pretty much concurred with TLS. The only person who vigorously opposed the idea was one whose opinion I hadn't really asked – the cheeky Yank. He pronounced himself absolutely aghast at the idea that I would even consider meeting up with Nic, and said that if he were in London he'd come over and chain himself in front of the doorway if that's what it took to keep me from doing so. It was his considered opinion that, by virtue of having broken it off with me via email, Nic was scum.

I couldn't help but be impressed with the apparent extent of his emotional investment. And met Nic just the same. And did indeed shag him. And did indeed feel very much worse in the morning, when, instead of pleading with me to stay not only for breakfast, but for the rest of his life, Nic informed me that we needed to get moving, as he had a succession of meetings in Highgate. There'd been a time when he'd have encouraged me to sleep in while he dashed off, but now apparently he didn't want me alone in his flat.

That night I cried myself to sleep, the next one, I drank myself to sleep, and the one after that I got an email from Nic advising me that he had returned to Florida, and was likely to be there for the next sixty days. But he'd enjoyed seeing me, and hoped we might be able to meet up again on his return.

Email is fast and convenient and generally fab, but there are things I miss about traditional writing-on-paper mail. Ripping it into a thousand pieces can be very much more cathartic than angrily clicking the Delete button.

I tried to lose myself in my work, but had too little in which to lose much of anything. The cheeky Yank, who'd risen slightly in my estimation by not scolding me about backsliding with Nic and then dropped back to slightly below where he'd started when I realised that the fervour with which he'd implored me to tell Nic to sod off had probably been just for show, thought the problem might be my Website. He would be willing to make it much more deluxe, as he put it, for only $300, or whatever that is in real money. I told him I'd consider it, even though I had no real intention of doing so, and was heartened to receive a response to my Matchmaker UK listing from a Canadian film maker who had a beard, but was otherwise presentable, and who knew that English sentences begin with capitalised letters and end with full stops. He hoped to meet me for a drink, and I immediately said yes.

The cheeky Yank reacted strangely. 'I absolutely forbid it,' he wrote. 'Mistress, you my woman now.' My hunch, given that his emails were invariably flawless grammatically, was that he was trying to sound like Porgy addressing Bess. Amused, I wrote back, 'I is?' Which apparently tickled him a treat. 'It's a rare pleasure,' he wrote, 'to encounter someone with Real Wit.'

Cheeky patronising git.

The Canadian documentary film maker turned out to have the shortest legs in the English-speaking world to go with the beard, and I found myself trying to think of an excuse to leap back aboard the train within ten minutes of meeting him. I was surprised to realise that I was eager to get home so I could share my impressions of him with the cheeky Yank, who, since we'd begun corresponding four months earlier, had jumped from one job to another to yet another, and was now working as a Web designer for the international consulting firm Deloitte & Touche, which he'd immediately rechristened Toilet & Douche. They seemed not to be keeping him very busy. He now wrote me at least half a dozen emails per day.

I looked at my bank statement, confirmed that I couldn't begin to afford to have him redesign my Website, took a deep breath, and asked him to do it anyway, praying that it would attract enough extra custom at least to cover the expense.

He'd moved without warning from *Porgy and Bess* to *The Story of O*, and was now demanding that I address him with the deference that accrued to his being my master. He, meanwhile, had taken to addressing me as 'slut'. I gave him the benefit of the doubt and assumed that he had tongue in cheek, and advised him of this assumption. There was no hint of playfulness in his reply. 'You will address me with the deference I demand, little whore,' he wrote, 'or leave me no choice but to punish you severely.'

The correspondence would have ended there and then, with me convinced that he was a nutter, if he hadn't redone my Website – spectacularly! – by the following morning. I was amazed, and told him so – and was relieved when he stepped out of his new guise to respond to my query about where to send his $300. 'Forget it,' he wrote, never suspecting that I'd made Cyril buy me perhaps the most extensive collection of fetish footwear in London's north-west suburbs. 'Get yourself some really good shoes IN YOUR OWN SIZE to wear for me instead.'

The new Website was breathtaking, and the phone would have rung off the hook had it not been my mobile. As it was, it rang a great, great deal, and I had the pleasure of conversing with some of the United Kingdom's principal wankers. I have since discussed the phenomenon with other mistresses, and discovered that it's absolutely par for the course for nine of ten callers to have no real intention of booking a session. They ring just for the thrill of spending a few minutes on the phone with a glamorous woman in latex and stiletto heels, although we are rather more commonly in denim and barefoot. A typical conversation with such a person is as follows.

'Hello, is that Chloe?'

'Mistress Chloe, yes.'

'I saw your advert. You look really sexy in that outfit. Are you wearing it right now?'

'We're not going to discuss what I'm wearing, I'm afraid. Are you interested in booking a session?'

'Um, yeah. A session. Great idea. Would you mind my asking what you *are* wearing now?'

I pause to sigh, and in the background hear the slurping of K-Y jelly being squeezed from a tube. 'What day can you come in?'

'Oh, I dunno. Monday? Thursday? Tuesday? Friday? Are you wearing the boots at least?'

'That's You with a capital y, if you don't mind. And I can see you on Wednesday between two and three, or between four-thirty and six.'

'Yes! Oh, yes!'

'Which?'

'Which what? Call me a name. Tell me you're going to twist my little pussy stick and call me a disgusting little sissy boy!'

'I'm going to pencil you in for Wednesday at two. You'll need to ring at least twenty-four hours in advance to confirm.'

'Oh, I'm so very close!'

'So you're based in London? Well, you can take either the Metropolitan line or . . .'

'Closer! Closer and closer!'

At around which juncture I usually hang up, secure in the knowledge that I'll never hear from him again.

In view of all of which, it's a rare treat to hear from someone who's actually phoning to set up an appointment, and using both hands. I came actually to look forward to the calls of one such person, Gareth.

'Hello, is it my privilege to be speaking to Mistress Chloe?' He was unusually well spoken.

'It is.'

The pitch of his voice went up a third in deference. 'Please, Mistress. Permission to speak.'

'You will save that level of obsequiousness for our face-to-face encounter. State your business.'

'Very good, Mistress. I am phoning in hopes of agreeing on a time that I might be able to come in for such a face-to-face encounter, Mistress, and wonder if Mistress might be able to see me next Thursday afternoon between three and six. I am aware of the tribute that Mistress requires, and of her expectation of promptness and impeccable hygiene.'

'Yes, a one-hour session on Thursday at three is available. You will need to confirm the appointment at least twenty-four hours in advance.'

'As indeed I will, Mistress. If it pleases Mistress, my name is

Gareth, and I am interested principally in severe caning, though I will eagerly welcome whatever punishment Mistress deems most appropriate for me. Thank you for your time, Mistress.'

Now was that so very hard? Short, sweet, all bases covered, respectful – the lot!

He didn't phone back twenty-four hours in advance of our appointment, but around thirty hours after our initial conversation – to notify me, very apologetically, that his schedule now made a Thursday appointment impossible. When I told him that I appreciated his considerateness, I could almost hear him blushing over the phone. 'Mistress,' he said softly, 'deserves every consideration.'

I quite enjoyed that, and told him so. To which he replied, 'Nothing could give me greater pleasure than to please Mistress.' Now I thought I could hear his eyes twinkling over the phone.

Ten days after I'd last spoken to him, Gareth finally phoned to say he was taking a one-week holiday from work, and that he hoped to see me on at least two of those days. We agreed on a time. He phoned twenty-four hours to the minute beforehand to confirm. 'I hope that Mistress will permit me to say how very, very excited I am finally to be able to come and see her.' I had to admit that I was pretty keen to meet him too. If he were half as attractive as charming, who knew what might happen?

Presenting himself precisely on time, he turned out to be even more handsome than charming – trim, around five foot ten, in a double-breasted grey wool suit that he wore well, wide-set blue eyes, light brown hair that may well have been moussed, a square jaw, and high cheekbones. Women adore men who know how to use mousse subtly. My first thought was that he was too pretty not to be made to dress up like a girl. My second was that I'd seen him somewhere before. It was hard to know for sure; good boy that he was, he kept his eyes scrupulously averted as he sank to one knee and held out his tribute on upraised palms.

I fretted in a way I never had before as I waited for him to remove his clothing and crawl into the dungeon. I had never been so attracted to any of my punters. I decided that the first step was to determine if he were married or otherwise spoken for. If not, I owed it to myself to arrange to see him out in the real world. Mr Nic Stoker could hang himself.

He looked better naked than anyone I'd ever had in my dungeon – and what a perfectly gorgeous implement! *Do not, under any circumstances, be married,* I thought. *I absolutely forbid it.* I kicked myself for not noticing if he'd worn a wedding ring when he came in.

I put a collar on him and marched him around in circles. He responded to the leash like a very well-trained horse. 'Well done, boy,' I announced. 'Wonderfully obedient.'

'Thank you, Mistress.'

'Tell me something, insect. Does your wife find you so wonderfully obedient?'

'I'm no longer married, Mistress. We divorced eighteen months ago, Mistress.'

'Your girlfriend then. Does *she*?'

'I have no girlfriend at present, Mistress.'

Be still, my beating heart. 'And may I ask why that is, insect?'

'After the breakup of my marriage, Mistress, it occurred

to me that it would be futile to become involved with another woman who doesn't share my . . . erotic predilections, Mistress.'

Our predilections, darling. And what a life of uninterrupted bliss we're going to have together. You come home from a hard day of being corporations' spokesman, and I'll put the collar on you and enjoy that perfectly luscious-looking cock of yours.

Which by now was in its full glory.

One never gives a punter what he's asked for in the early going. Rather, one tantalises him with the promise of it while hurting him gently in some other way. I thought I'd strap him to the St Andrew's and see how sensitive his nipples were. I snapped my fingers and indicated where he was to stand. He had a really nice smell about him too, clean, subtle. Once again it occurred to me that I knew him from somewhere.

When I had him on the cross I told him to close his eyes. I wanted to take a long look at him from straight on.

Very, very familiar, somehow, and yet . . .

Oh, Jesus!

There was no denying that it was Derek Whatsit, the notorious spokesman for Moskowitz Shoes, the charming, handsome face of animal abuse in the service of human greed.

'When did you stop calling yourself Derek, insect?' His eyes shot open full of panic, and any trace of hope I might have had that it was a case of mistaken identity based on a breathtaking resemblance went out of the window. He closed them again and murmured, 'I don't know what you mean, Mistress,' but it was too late.

Oh, the things I wanted to say! The outrage I wanted to

express! The frustration! And the only way I could was to betray the unwritten covenant on which all my dealings with submissives were based, a conception of privilege very closely akin to that which priests take into the confession booth, solicitors into the courtroom, and doctors into their surgeries.

Sod that. With his good looks and limitless charm, who knows how many minds Derek Whatsit had kept from being changed about animal rights over the years, and how much horror had been got away with in the face of the resulting public apathy? God knows he would get his caning – a caning that he would deserve more than anyone I'd ever had up on my cross – but he would get a piece of Mistress's mind into the bargain.

I had him open his mouth wide, stuck a dildo in it and secured it with tape. I prayed that I hadn't discarded the dog-walking business card my old fellow activist Liz Compton had given me the afternoon I'd encountered her on the train after my *Playboy Channel* shooting. I hadn't – there it was, rumpled but eminently legible, in the bottom of my bag.

I rang her home and got an answer machine. I tried her mobile. It rang three times and my heart sank. But then she answered.

She didn't know who I was at first. Standing out in front of Noble Furs, we'd all known one another by first name, and there must have been half a dozen Claires in the mix. I reminded her of our meeting on the train a couple of months before. 'I was looking very much a slapper that day,' I reminded her.

'Oh, of course!' she exulted. '*Claire!*'

It occurred to me that this was going to involve my blowing

my cover – and that my cover was of scant importance in comparison to The Greater Good. I asked if Lizzy happened to have a copy of *The Animals Film* in her video collection. My heart sank again when she said she was pretty sure she'd lent it to someone ages ago and not got it back. She went to have a look, and was gone for ever. If I held Derek too long against his will, would I be liable for prosecution of some sort? I imagined that he was on a first-name basis with some of the most powerful solicitors in the UK. Christ, what was I doing?

'No,' Lizzy finally said, doubling my fondness for her in the wink of an eye, 'I *have* got it. She must have brought it back.'

'I can't tell you exactly why I want it,' I said, realising that revealing Derek's visit to Mistress Chloe would be an ethical lapse I couldn't rationalise, 'but I very much need to borrow it from you, Lizzy – this minute.'

There was an extended silence her end. 'And there's no one else you can get it from?'

'No one. Honestly, Lizzy. I know this is a terrible imposition. I wouldn't ask if it weren't extremely important. Please know it isn't for me, but for all of us.'

She sighed. And agreed to bring it right over. She had a car, bless her heart, and I had so much to do in the few minutes it would take for her to arrive.

I rang Wendy upstairs. She wasn't home. I tried her mobile. Thank God. I told her I urgently needed to watch a videotape in her lounge. She was very dubious. I told her that it was of the utmost importance. She asked if it would be just me watching, or if there'd be a slave as well. She wasn't at all pleased by my answer. 'This means I won't be able to come home,' she said. 'Obviously I won't have Oscar and Alanis walking into the lounge while you and a punter are in there.' I told her I knew that I was asking an awful lot, and that I wouldn't dream of doing so if it weren't of life-and-death importance. She didn't need to know that the lives I was referring to were animals'. She sighed and asked me to ring when I was finished.

I hurried back in to Derek, turned him round on the cross, gave him a taste of the cane, and told him there would be more if he were a good boy. My phone rang. Lizzy was already at the front door. I gave Derek a good hard one and went up to get the tape. As I knew it would, Lizzy's mouth dropped open at the sight of me in my kit. I didn't take the time to explain, but only thanked her, assured her that I would make it up to her one day, and went back inside. I put the tape in the VCR, turned on the TV, sorted out the workings of the system, and went downstairs for Derek, handcuffing his wrists behind his back, and attaching cuffs to his ankles as well. I didn't want him even to think of trying to escape. It was important that he pay rapt attention.

'Have you been a very naughty boy, Gareth?' I demanded, twisting his earlobe.

With the dildo still in his mouth, he nodded eagerly. 'Far naughtier than you've even begun to realise,' I said, and pulled him to his feet. With his feet chained within nine inches of one another, he didn't move very quickly, but I finally got him upstairs. There was confusion in his eyes. His erection had wilted. I got him into the lounge and pushed him back into a chair.

'I know who you are,' I said. 'It seemed for eighteen months as though you were on Sky News every other night. I suspect you know, deep in your heart, that the corporation you spoke for so convincingly is evil, but just in case there's any doubt in your mind, I want you to watch something.' There was indignation in his eyes now, indignation and betrayal.

Bugger his indignation.

I started the tape. He made it through the electrocution of the elephant, and then opted for civil disobedience of his own, closing his eyes.

I paused the tape. 'I can't make you watch it, Derek. And I acknowledge that I'm bending the rules by trying to get you to. But I will mention that this house belongs to a good friend of mine who happens to be an editor at the *News of the World*. If you don't watch, and attentively, I'll leave you here for her to find. My guess is that she's seen you on TV as well.'

If looks could kill! Oh, the malice in his gorgeous blue eyes. I started the tape back up.

I hadn't seen it in a couple of years at least, and had forgotten how awful it was. I forgot about Derek and was lost in my own feelings, my own outrage and sadness.

The tape ended. He looked shell-shocked. He didn't turn to me, but just stared at the TV. I peeled the tape off his mouth and removed the dildo. He still didn't look at me. 'God, I'm sorry,' he said. 'I can't tell you how sorry.' Was he saying what he thought I wanted to hear – and what he thought would get him out of the house before a *News of the World* editor discovered him – or expressing genuine contrition? There was no way for me to know. It might well have been that he didn't know either.

I gave him back his money. He dressed quickly and left without another word between us. I burst into tears.

He made no further attempt at communication. He doesn't seem to have attempted retaliation, and if, as I'd dared to hope he might, he contacted the media to repudiate his association with Moskowitz, it has gone unreported.

CHAPTER NINETEEN

In Bondage to Another, and Suddenly So Free

'd been staggered by the cheeky Yank's generosity, but it was time to get things clarified. 'I very much appreciate your kindness,' I wrote, 'but I have to say that the whole *Story of O* thing is beginning to chafe a bit. Given that I am accustomed to holding the leash, rather than having it attached to me, I would ask that you leave it out, and immediately.' If I were one of those people who loaded her emails with hieroglyphics, I'd have put in a :-) to indicate my own lightheartedness, but I'm not, and left it to him to sort out.

The email he sent in response consisted entirely of a URL, that of a story written by a submissive American woman, Anna

Zsubone, about a meeting in a San Francisco hotel room with a dominant man she'd met on line. It was really quite sexy. The guy, whom she knew only as Master, told her she was to leave her hotel-room door unlocked and wait for him on all fours atop her bed in a black lace basque, seamed stockings, very high heels, black nylon opera gloves, too much makeup, and rhinestone earrings. (Say what you might about the guy, he knew what he liked.) And she was to keep her eyes scrupulously closed during the whole of the encounter. If at any point he noticed that she'd opened them, he would immediately push her out into the hall in her scandalous attire and lock her out of her own room.

There was something about that I found quite thrilling.

She'd brought her collection of 'toys' along – whips and paddles and crops and floggers – and he'd used all of them on her, taunting and fondling her between blows in exactly the right proportion, keeping her just on the ecstasy side of the border between it and agony. While making her take him in her mouth, he'd phoned – or pretended to phone – room service, and had informed whomever answered that there was an insatiable little slut up in Room 518 who would very happily fellate any member of the staff in need of relief.

When, tiring of her, he'd abruptly left her, she'd found herself weeping in the most rapturous, cleansing way at great length. In the end, she wrote, she'd somehow wound up feeling absolved.

That resonated. In the course of my career to date as a dominatrix, I'd divined that absolution was exactly what many of my punters most hoped to find in my dungeon, albeit unwittingly in most cases. They had their fantasies – perfectly natural for them, but clearly very far afield in most cases from those of their mates. Living in a culture that's pretty constricted about how one can express oneself erotically, they consequently felt a deep sense of shame, for which they needed to be punished. When they visited a professional dominatrix, and were simultaneously titillated and beaten, they received instant absolution.

It had occurred to me, God knows, that I needed some of my own – that fundamentally I wasn't dominant at all, but submissive – but I wasn't about to expose that part of me to just anyone, or even, in fact, to anyone I'd been with over the course of my romantic history. If I were going to submit, it could be only to a man of unattenuated self-confidence and power, vast physical attractiveness, and formidable intellect.

Now it can be told. I had indeed looked at the dominant male listings on such sites as kinkycontacts.com – and had nearly died laughing (through my tears). The ones who knew how to spell were little twerps. The gorgeous ones didn't know how to spell. The ones with panache – those whose photos depicted them in form-fitting black latex, glaring menacingly at the photographer rather than grinning sappily – were looking for other men.

So could my cheeky Yank be my knight in black latex? He seemed to have self-confidence enough for five – with sufficient arrogance left over for another three. He wrote a witty and literate email, but at fifty-two, or whatever he was, if he wasn't past it, he was certainly hurtling towards it. And, in spite of his encounter with Ms Zsubone, I'd always got the impression that he was submissive, that his cheekiness was that of someone who hoped to be slapped down for it. Judging from the photos he'd sent, the years hadn't been as kind as they might have been. Looking at the most recent of the lot, I'd asked myself if I'd make meaningful eye contact with him if I glimpsed him across a crowded pub. I hadn't been at all sure I would.

All that said, I decided in the end to play along. 'In accordance with His directive,' I wrote back, 'Master's obedient little whore went this afternoon to Camden Town and bought a pair of black platform sandals with eight-inch heels that she looks forward to modelling for Master.'

He liked that *very* much. Indeed, he would later tell me that he nearly fell out of San Francisco when he read it. He responded immediately, demanding that I supply photographs of myself in the new footwear.

I continued to play along. Out came my little digital camera. Out came my slinkiest fetishwear. In, I hoped, stayed Fiona, as the only place I could take a full-length photo of myself was in the hall, rather than behind the closed doors I'd have much preferred.

He was very pleased. 'I'm so looking forward,' he wrote, 'to getting my hands on you, slut.' He demanded my phone number. I provided it. He told me he would be ringing his little whore at a particular time, and was right on the dot. The first words I ever heard him say were, 'On your knees, you brazen little tart.' His confidence was exhilarating. His voice was very soft, just as La Zsubone had described it, very far from traditionally gruff and masculine, but he used the language well, never seemed at a loss for words, and was quite wonderfully tyrannical. It was a better climax than I'd had with Nic actually in me. And I enjoyed the fact that we never came out of character – after I'd climaxed, he didn't ask how the weather was in London (as though one need ever ask), but simply whispered, 'Good night, slut,' and hung up.

I gave it enough time for his testosterone level to revert to something closer to normal, and pointed out via email that he was living with someone, and had in fact lived with her for over a decade. He wrote back to say that it was crumbling. They were grievously mismatched erotically. Though she loved him enough to indulge his fetishes every now and again, it was always unmistakably with considerable reluctance, and anything kinkier was very much out of the question. And it turned out that, years after abandoning his dreams of pop stardom, he continued to compose and record original songs, which she made no bones about disdaining. He was self-conscious about his weak singing voice, and she'd apparently been unable to think of anything good to say about it over the course of their many years together. He had written a short story collection the previous year, and she'd been insufficiently interested to ask to read it.

During the fortnight she would spend studying the native flora of Hawaii (poor thing!) in two months' time, he proposed to summon me to San Francisco. I couldn't pretend that I didn't find the prospect thrilling, and eagerly began researching bargain airfares. But then it occurred to me that it would be madness to dash off to the west coast of America for two weeks when I was just beginning to attract substantial numbers of punters.

For nearly two weeks, he sulked – or at least wrote very little email. Then I discovered that he'd changed jobs yet again, having concluded that Toilet & Douche offered insufficient outlet for his boundless genius. He was now ensconced in the senior Web designership of a bold little dot-com startup that was going to revolutionise the way news was distributed over the Internet or something. He wasn't terribly clear about it himself, but they'd got him a wonderful state-of-the-art Macintosh, on which he'd just installed ICQ, and he wanted me to talk dirty to him virtually while he designed the bold little startup's Website.

Such was his genius that he was able to tear himself away from what he was doing every ninety seconds to describe the erotic degradations that awaited me in California. Then he abruptly disappeared for a long while. I was just about to shut down my own computer and cry myself to sleep when he came back on line to tell me to forget about California. He had just been sacked in the wake of the bold little startup's third major reorganisation in the two weeks that he'd worked for it. He was coming to London.

You might wait until you've been invited, I thought. But then I reflected on it. Hadn't I fancied myself attracted to exactly the sort of man who didn't wait to be invited?

We had some very spicy ICQ dialogues in the weeks leading up to his visit, but only one more phone call – he was nothing if not frugal – and that out of character, which is to say as ourselves. I found him quite fun to talk to, droll and engaging. He spoke in complete sentences and used great big deluxe words, but apparently not self-consciously.

My birthday arrived. I celebrated with friends at a chic little Italian place in Hampstead, and was having a glorious time until my old boyfriend Vladimir showed up with his most recent girlfriend, whom he knew me to loathe. She was even more of a mess than he, and I was consumed by dread that she would pull him the rest of the way down the drain with her. The sight of her ruined my mood. I spent half the balance of the evening sulking and the other half seething.

I wrote to the cheeky Yank about it the next morning, expecting that he'd toe the party line, as had The Lovely Sally, who'd taken Vladimir aside and given him a good talking to about his woeful insensitivity. I bemoaned the fact that, because Vladimir had brought his horrible girlfriend along, it had been impossible for me to celebrate my birthday with him for the first time since we'd been an item back in the Palaeolithic Era.

Far from toeing the line, the cheeky Yank gave me a stern talking to. 'He wanted to celebrate your birthday with you, girlfriend,' he wrote, sounding like a bad moment on Rikki Lake, 'but you preferred to be petulant about his choice of companion. If anybody spoiled your birthday, it was the birthday girl.' Piling indignity on indignity, he said that my account had inspired him to begin writing a song that he hoped one day to entitle 'Me at My Worst'. And I was to write Vladimir a letter of apology for my vindictive childishness.

Well, that was definitely that. Once again I cursed my inability to tear an email up into a million shreds. Had he been nearby, I'd have played squash with the arrogant bastard's bollocks, my lifelong aversion to sport notwithstanding. But as the day progressed, I found myself wondering more and more if he weren't right – and eventually decided that he was.

Not only droll and literate and kinky, but maybe even wise.

I couldn't write the letter, though, and I told him so.

There was a limit to how much I was prepared to submit to anyone.

'No, slut,' he wrote back, 'you're mistaken. The only limits are those I set. Now, because you have resisted Me, you will not only write the letter to Vladimir, but one to Anna Zsubone as well, telling her that it was her piece about our rendezvous that inspired you to realise your place.'

Oh, definitely. I was really about to write a congratulatory letter to a woman of whom I couldn't help but be jealous – and as soon as I finished it, I was going to go buy myself a couple of Big Macs and some Moskowitz pumps and see if the market research company in Eastcote would have me back. I told him I couldn't do it, much as I wanted to please him.

'Do you realise what's at stake here?' he wrote back. 'When your Master gives you a directive, there is one and only one appropriate response – immediate and complete compliance. Is that quite understood?'

I must have sat and stared at those words in the little box on my screen for two minutes. I, a strong, opinionated, intelligent, independent woman – a professional dominatrix, for Christ's sake – was not going to allow myself to be bullied like this. How would I ever be able to lead another naked slave into my dungeon on a leash? It was non-negotiable, utterly out of the question. And I saw that what I'd typed was, 'Yes, Master. Understood.' As I clicked the Send button, I felt a wave of exhilaration such as I had never experienced before. How, in embracing my own bondage to another, could I suddenly feel so free?

I was paralysed, as though in a dream, immobile in my

chair, simultaneously terrified and rapturous. It took him what seemed hours to type back, 'Well done, slut. You have pleased your Master.'

His arrival in London grew ever nearer, and then, after an eternity, was twenty-four hours away. I went to see my might-have-been dominatrix hairdresser, the stalwart Claire, and asked her to make my hair bigger than it had ever been before. To go with my Angie Dickinson bouffant, I was to make myself up as though to walk the streets of Soho in 1966. Which is to say that he very much liked the harsh too-much-liquid-eyeliner look of the Ronettes and that whole lot. If fewer than three strange men offered me money for sex between the car park and the arrival area, I would be severely punished.

We planned our first face-to-face meeting in great detail. I would arrive at Heathrow well in advance of his flight, and, brazen little tart that I was, offer to fellate two men at random while I waited, thus ensuring that there would be dried semen on my clothing when he finally emerged from customs. He needed something to punish me for, didn't he?

In the end, we decided that we would spend our first few minutes together out of character. I wanted to embrace him. He even said that he would allow me to wear shoes in which I could actually walk, but only with the understanding that for the duration of his stay with me, I was never to wear heels of less than four inches, nor ever to have bare legs. Every morning I was to put on fresh black stockings for him.

We sent a flurry of ICQ messages back and forth in the hours before he was to leave for San Francisco International. I was to understand that the years had stolen every last trace of his earlier rock star good looks, that his face was full of ghastly furrows, that his hairline had been sneaking implacably towards the top of his head. And he, in turn, was to keep in mind that I had always been small-breasted. He assured me that my famously long slim legs were of much greater interest to him.

He looked dazed when he finally emerged from customs, and who could blame him, as he'd begun his journey twenty-two hours before. He'd told me that he was six foot one, but I'd somehow not realised how tall that was. He seemed very tall indeed, and fit, and not the time-ravaged embarrassment he'd led me to expect. Not seeing me among the teeming, mostly swarthy, masses awaiting flights from Karachi, he stood there looking forlorn. And then, as he'd tell me a few minutes later, he saw my high heels among the tangle of legs. And then we were hurrying to one another, and embracing.

And trying, for several hours (or so it seemed) to find my car. I could have sworn I'd left it on the first level of the car park, but there was no sign of it there, nor on the second, or even on the third. What a wonderful impression I was probably making! 'You understand, of course, that you'll have to be severely punished for this, don't you, slut?' he stopped me at one point to ask. But there was mischief in his eyes and one corner of his mouth betrayed a barely suppressed ironic smirk.

It *was* on the first level. He put his bags in the boot. We got in and he demanded that I spread my knees and keep my eyes straight ahead. He'd agreed to allow me to wear shoes I could actually walk in, but had insisted on a suspender belt, stockings, and no knickers under my coat. He made a soft sound of delight as he confirmed my compliance. 'Gorgeous,' he said. 'Even prettier than expected.' His hand was on my knee. And then, taking its own sweet time, at my stocking top. He gently touched the soft white flesh above it. My breathing became shallow. He laughed at my excitement, and that made me more excited. 'What an utterly shameless little slut you are,' he said, 'allowing someone you've only just met to touch you like this.

'Aren't you, slut?'

'Yes, Master.'

'And I imagine that if I were to move My hand even higher, I'd discover that you're very wet. Is that not right, clarissa?' He'd decided that Claire sounded insufficiently diminutive for a brazen little slut.

'Master is always right, Master.' And he was. I was absolutely sopping.

He took my hand and placed it between his legs. Most promising.

'I have a theory as to why you're so wet, clarissa,' he said matter-of-factly. I waited for him to continue, but he had all the time in the world. I realised that it was his timing, the spaces he left, that made the things he said to me so thrilling. It was nearly musical, like a jazz saxophonist setting up successive phrases with rests of different durations. It finally occurred to me what he was waiting for: 'Yes, Master?'

His hand was still and very, very warm on my thigh above my stocking. He leaned closer so he could speak even more softly. 'I think the reason that you're so wet, clarissa, is that you're a little bitch in heat.' I shuddered with excitement. His finger was in me now, teasing my swollen clitoris. And then, a moment later, it was out of me.

'Take me home, little whore,' he said, pushing my knees together.

It was hilarious, in its way, how we went in a wink from being Master and clarissa so steamily to being a cheeky Yank visitor to Britain and his hostess. Forty-five seconds after he'd had his finger in me, after a shorter face-to-face acquaintance than any in my history, we were talking about the weather, and then, as we got on to the motorway, about his speculation that municipal ordinance must require that there be an establishment called Tandoori Express every 100 feet in Hayes.

Then we were back in picturesque Ruislip, and Master reappeared. I began opening the boot of my car. He stopped me. 'Later,' he said, taking me firmly under the arm, pushing me towards the front door – through which I very, very, very much hoped Fiona wasn't about to burst on one of her bimonthly expeditions into the world outside her half of the house.

Guess which room we headed for immediately. He didn't toss me down on the bed, though, but instead told me to put on the shoes I'd bought in Camden. He had all the time in the world. I was nearly as tall as him now, and he loved that.

He pushed me face first against the wall and roughly pulled off my coat. One moment he was drawing circles on my bare white bottom with his fingertip, and the next slapping it hard. It surprised me so much that I nearly forgot how I was meant to respond. 'Thank you, Master. Please, may I have another?'

'Another, you shameless little baggage?' he purred, his

lips an inch from my ear. 'Well, I certainly think that can be arranged.' Oh, did it smart. And oh, how lovely the smarting. Thank you, Master, indeed.

He unzipped his trousers, pulled my hand back, and filled it with his cock and balls. 'Let's see how a shameless little tart fondles her Master,' he growled, and I obliged with great enthusiasm.

He spun me round and only now tossed me on the bed. He loomed over me, licking his lips. He still had all the time in the world. He wasn't the biggest I'd ever seen up close, but he may well have been in the Top 5, and in terms of staying power, he proceeded to claim a spot on the top of the heap. We were at it for hours. Literally. It was as though he hadn't made love in years and was trying to make up for it all in one afternoon. And then he finally climaxed, surprisingly demurely, and we lay there for another month or so, corroborating in person what we'd already inferred virtually – that we got one another's jokes, arid though most of them were. And I felt pretty certain that I was in love.

He wasn't much of a drinker, and didn't seem to be addicted to anything else. He was incredulous about the extent to which Britons are still allowed to smoke in public places, his hatred of the smell of cigarette smoke being a match for my own. Standing in queues, he kept himself to himself, in marked, blessed contrast to my ex-husband. He bathed conscientiously, bewailing my lack of a power shower. He found the whole idea of my being a professional dominatrix terribly sexy. And I, in turn, found that I didn't just love him, but also quite liked him.

He thought that, in his ability to demand my demurral whenever it pleased him to, we had a built-in safety mechanism that guaranteed a harmonious relationship. He sussed, in spite of my best efforts to conceal it, that I was iffy on the idea. I had to trust him not to invoke his status as my Master whimsically, but only in moments of grave danger to our relationship. I admitted that I didn't know, when push came to shove, if I'd be able to manage it, and reminded him that I am a strong, independent, opinionated woman, one who had made the spokesman for the British Field Sports Society blink. 'If you were anything less than strong, independent, and opinionated,' he said, smirking in that maddening, often very sexy way of his, 'your submission would have no value. Am I not right, slut?'

'Master is always right, Master.'

I had been accustomed to hearing Fiona shuffle with the ponderousness of the perpetually despondent from her bedroom to her lounge, and then back again, and to her agonised smoker's cough, but I wasn't at all used to re-enactments of World War II, which is what I was hearing now, in the second of the cheeky Yank's two weeks in London. It sounded as though heavy furniture were being pushed over, and glass shattering. I wondered if I should go up, and decided not to. An armistice was apparently declared.

And then rescinded, and the carnage far worse – or at least louder – than before. She had played Steely Dan's *Katy Lied* approximately 150 times a day since a friend had lent it to her a month and a half before, and I'd uttered not a syllable of protest, but this was more than one sibling could ask another to endure.

I waited for the various armies to rush their dead and wounded off the battleground and tapped lightly on her door. She didn't respond. I tapped once more, rather less gently. Were those sobs I heard? I tapped a third time and she bellowed, 'Piss off,' putting such a strain on her tobacco-ravaged lungs that she proceeded to cough violently for twenty seconds. I couldn't turn my back on whatever was going on, and let myself in.

She had indeed been pushing things over, and hurling plates and ashtrays at the walls. The floor was strewn not only with the usual cigarette butts and the remains of long-forgotten snacks, but with shattered glass as well, and overturned tables and chairs. Fiona stood gaping at the devastation in astonishment, and then let out an awful anguished wail and hurled the large shard of ashtray she found just beyond the couch at her framed reproduction of Van Gogh's *The Undergrowth With Two Figures, June 1890*. She dropped to her knees and resumed sobbing.

I made my way over to her and gently touched her head. She threw her arms round my legs and wept. I wanted to kneel beside her and hold her, but she had my legs pressed so hard together that I couldn't. When she let go of me and went foraging for something else to hurl, I was finally able to get a good grip on her. Her breath was the worst I'd encountered since Bogweed Bunion's maths class.

'For Christ's sake, Fi. What is it?'

She acted as though it were the most preposterous question she'd ever heard. 'What is it? What fucking *is* it? Well, take a bloody guess.'

In the past twelve years, only one thing about her life had changed. 'Roger?'

Her eyes became slits, her voice a diabolical growl. 'Don't ever speak his name in my presence again, Claire. Not bloody ever!' She whirled round, found the whisky bottle that she'd apparently spent the afternoon emptying into herself, and was about to hurl it at the window when I managed to grab it away.

She collapsed to the ground like a marionette whose strings have been snipped and tried to pull out handfuls of her own hair. Once again I restrained her.

She went catatonic on me, staring numbly at nothing at all. 'Fiona?' I finally said. 'Do tell me about it, won't you? Fi?'

'I expected too much,' she finally mumbled, addressing thin air. 'I expected a man to keep his promises.' Now she looked at me, and her eyes focused. 'That'll be the bloody day, though, won't it?'

I hesitated to draw her out, for fear that the windows might not survive. I just held on to her until she was ready on her own.

'He was married, of course. He never kept that from me. But he said they hadn't shagged in ages, in bloody years. He was fed up with it. He was going to leave her for me. That's what he said, that he was going to leave her for me. We were good together at the start. We were bloody marvellous. I never imagined I could enjoy sex so much.'

A combination of the thought of Fiona with Roger having at it, her breath, and the stench of the countless overturned ashtrays made me giddy, but I stayed the course.

She began yet again to cry, very softly. 'I tried to give him everything he wanted. I loved him, Claire. But the things he began asking for . . . you wouldn't believe how perverted they were.'

Uh-oh.

She crawled around for a moment until she found a cigarette butt of ignitable length. Inhaling it got her coughing again. 'He wanted me to dress up like one of those dunno-what-you-call-'ems, those whatsits in black leather tat and boots, and to put a dog collar on him and lead him around on his hands and knees. He wanted me to call him names. Well, I'm very sorry, but I fail to see anything even remotely erotic about that. What I find it is sick and disgusting.'

It occurred to me that Fiona and I weren't likely to have an intimate heart-to-heart about my profession any time terribly soon.

I took the cheeky Yank to Torture Gardens' big tenth anniversary celebration down in south London. He'd very much enjoyed the idea of removing my top when we got inside, handcuffing my hands behind my back, and leading me around on a leash. The idea got me damp too, but I fretted that it might be bad for business – Mistress Chloe had a reputation to uphold. He was disappointed, but didn't invoke Masterly privilege.

I went to the bar when we arrived while he gallantly queued up for the cloakroom. In the twenty minutes it took him to deposit our coats and street clothes, I had already attracted two worshippers, the first a one-armed transvestite in a pink satin frock called Roxanne, and a moustachioed little lurker who claimed to have no name, each down on his or her knees licking my ankle boots. I couldn't read the look on the cheeky

Yank's face. At first I thought it was just surprise, but then I thought embarrassment, and then delight, and then annoyance. Afraid of finding out it was the last, I abruptly stepped away from my two worshippers.

And I thought Mr Nic Stoker had eyed me up and down brazenly the night we met face-to-face. It had been nothing compared to how the cheeky Yank was eyeing me now, the first time he'd ever seen me in full dominatrix kit – my black pleather officer's cap, platinum blonde bob wig, black PVC minidress, matching PVC gloves, black stockings, and the shoes from Camden Town. He looked like a little boy in a sweet shop. He pulled me to him and kissed me lightly, but at great length, on the lips. I felt as though in a film, as though the world were whirling around us. Our lips finally parted. 'Whose are you, clarissa?' he whispered into my ear.

I put it together now. My looking so ravishing had made him territorial, possessive, pre-emptively jealous. I looked into his eyes at length, thought I saw what I'd been hoping to see, and replied, 'You will address Me as Mistress, boy.'

If he'd looked like a boy in a model aeroplane store a moment before, he looked like a boy in ten model aeroplane stores now. His smirk had lost its superior, mocking quality. It was now that of one who'd been seen through, and the longer I glared at him, the more obvious it became. I grabbed his hand, turned my back on him, and led him, just for the joy of leading him, through the crowd to the other end of the huge room.

He leaned towards me to kiss me again. At the last moment, I turned my head away. He was confused and embarrassed – and loving every bit of it. He leaned again. Again I turned away. And again. And a fourth time. 'You never learn, do you, boy?' It was a voice he hadn't heard before, the haughty, excoriating snarl I use in my dungeon. And it made his mouth drop open.

I told him to get me a drink. Off he went, without a moment's protest, smiling ecstatically. By the time he returned, there was another lurker kissing my boots while I tapped his back with the crop he'd provided. The cheeky Yank couldn't conceal his delight.

I spun on my heel and headed upstairs without explanation. There was no need for me to look back. I knew he'd be right behind me. And I was right. Mistress is always right.

I found the playroom. There were stocks lining it. At three of the five stations, mistresses were flogging men. At another, a portly white-haired man was paddling an anorexic-looking woman. I had only to step over to the unused stocks for three men nearly to trample one another trying to put their necks and wrists in it. I secured the nimblest of them and accepted a cat-o'-nine-tails from the room's attendant. I watched my cheeky Yank closely as I very slowly dragged the cat over my boy's bare back – and then, without warning, brought it hissing down on him. His mouth was open again.

I released my first playmate and beckoned with a movement of my black PVC finger to one of the crowd of around half a dozen that had formed in a semicircle behind me. On this one, I used the crop, crisscrossing his upper back with weals. Each time I struck him, he screamed, 'Please, Mistress, another!' a little more convincingly than the time before. My cheeky Yank was awestruck.

I stepped over to him and held his chin in my hand, and

kissed him tenderly on the lips. 'I love you,' I told him for the first time. And then I left him standing there, looking as though he'd glimpsed Jesus, and resumed asserting my supremacy among all the dominant goddesses of London.

Afterwards, in the cab back to Ruislip, he told me what I already knew – that he'd had no idea of my power and charisma, and that he wanted very much for me to mark him, just as I had the boys in the stocks. 'I love you enough,' he said, 'not only to allow you to mark me too, but to beg you for it.'

And he did. And so he continues to do.

Claire Mansfield

In memory of Marlin Dog – my beloved baby.

Thanks to: MB and DP for their exceptional and unwavering love and support; G, the finest of brothers; Debra, Angela Crowe and Sally-Anne Smith, 'The Lovelies', for friendship above and beyond the call of duty; AJ and Stephanie, my godchildren; Pete 'Too loud!' Vas and Cobweb, dearest Furry Face; Dave ESB Fuller, for being Dave ESB Fuller; Paul Denham, my old mate – see you in the Ship; Hania Wodzinski, for bailing me out when no-one else would; Jackie, Fritz, Topsy, Toby, Motchka, Gibson, Hally and Gally, Damson and Mishka, always in our hearts.

Never forgetting: Keith Gerrard; Faebhean Kwest; Rock FM; Raiders FM; Tony Williams; Julie Denton; Monty Zero; London Animal Action; Mistress Caprice; Mistress Caz; Lornet Prather; Lizzy and Ed; Lady Lindsay and Queen Juliana; and all the ex-boyfriends who inadvertently contributed.

John Mendelssohn

Thanks to: Toni Emerson of the Central Florida College of Botany, School of Alternative Sexuality, for her indispensable insights and love; Kathleen Guneratne, for having single-handedly saved my birthday in 1997, and for her precious friendship; Richard d'Andrea for enabling the recording of the Mistress's extremely good CD, 'Like a Moth to Its Flame' (http://www.heartless.com/MistressChloe/mothFlame.html), even though it's by no means his own cup of tea; Lewis Segal, for his early mentorship, both professional and personal; Richard Riegel, and David McGee, for their friendship; Chef Bill Allen for his hospitality; Greg Shaw and John Kordosh for their generous assessments of my writing; Rick Snyder and Harper Payne for their recent encouragement of my music; gina whore for her unwavering good sportswomanship; and to dedicate his work on this book, as on all things, to Brigitte.